Gardening

www.thegoodwebguide.co.uk

thegoodwebguide

Gardening

Sue Little

The Good Web Guide Limited • London

First Published in Great Britain in 2000 by The Good Web Guide Limited
Broadwall House, 21 Broadwall, London, SE1 9PL

www.thegoodwebguide.co.uk

Email:feedback@thegoodwebguide.co.uk

© 2000 The Good Web Guide Ltd

Text © 2000 Susan Little

Original series concept by Steve Bailey.

Cover photo © Reider and Walsh/Photonica

10 9 8 7 6 5 4 3 2 1

A catalogue record for this book is available from the British Library.

ISBN 1-903282-00-4

Project Editor Michelle Clare

Additional reviews by Jacqueline Wapshott

Design by Myriad Creative Ltd

Typesetting and additional design by Karen Brain

Printed in Italy at LEGO S.p.A.

Contents

The Good Web Guides

The World Wide Web is a vast resource, with millions of sites on every conceivable subject. There are people who have made it their mission to surf the net: cyber communities have grown, and people have formed relationships and even married on the net.

However, the reality for most people is that they don't have the time or inclination to surf the net for hours on end. Busy people want to use the internet for quick access to information. You don't have to spend hours on the internet looking for answers to your questions and you don't have to be an accomplished net surfer or cyber wizard to get the most out of the web. It can be a quick and useful resource if you are looking for specific information.

The Good Web Guides have been published with this in mind. To give you a head start in your search, our researchers have looked at hundreds of sites and what you will find in the Good Web Guides is a collection of reviews of the best we've found.

The Good Web Guide recommendation is impartial and all the sites have been visited several times.

Reviews are focused on the website and what it sets out to do, rather than an endorsement of a company, or their product. A small but beautiful site run by a one-man band may be rated higher than an ambitious but flawed site run by a mighty organisation.

Relevance to the UK-based visitor is also given a high premium: tantalising as it is to read about purchases you can make in California, because of delivery charges, import duties and controls it may not be as useful as a local site.

Our reviewers considered a number of questions when reviewing the sites, such as: How quickly do the sites/individual pages download? Can you move around the site easily and get back to where you started, and do the links work? Is the information up to date and accurate? And is the site pleasing to the eye and easy to read? More importantly, we also asked whether the site has something distinctive to offer, whether it be entertainment, inspiration or pure information. On the basis of the answers to these questions sites are given ratings out of five. As we aim only to include sites that we feel are of serious interest there are very few low-rated sites.

Bear in mind that the collection of reviews you see here are just a snapshot of the sites at a particular time. The process of choosing and writing about sites is rather like painting the Forth Bridge: as each section appears complete, new sites are launched and others are modified. When you've registered at the Good Web Guide site (see p.159 for further details) you can check out the reviews of new sites and updates of existing ones, or even have them emailed to you. By using the disc at the back of the book or registering on our site, you'll find hot links to all the sites listed, so you can just click and go without needs to type the addresses accurately into your browser.

As this is the first edition of the Good Web Guide, all our sites have been reviewed by the author and research team, but we'd like to know what you think. Contact us via the website or email feedback@thegoodwebguide.co.uk. You are welcome to recommend sites, quibble about the ratings, point out changes and inaccuracies or suggest new features to assess.

You can find us at www.thegoodwebguide.co.uk

User Key text	
UK / US	Country of origin
£	Subscription required
R	Registration required
🔒	Secure online ordering.

Introduction

What could the internet possibly offer the keen gardener? It would seem that most gardeners don't have enough hours in the day left over to search the web after dragging themselves away from their borders and beds, let alone building their own homepage. In fact there is a surprising number of websites out there on an eclectic range of subjects. The beauty of the web is its diversity and you can guarantee that whatever your interest in gardening there will be a site that can help you. You can find a site to suit your tastes no matter how obscure it seems. Finding the most rewarding ones can be a tiring adventure of trial and error.

Enter 'garden' in a search engine or 'roses' or 'slugs' to see what comes up. You may receive tens of thousands of suggestions, presented in no particular order.

There are sites on gardening in general, cottage gardening, urban gardening for everyone from the serious plantaholic to the armchair dreamer. Some sites are academic, others inspirational, or whimsical. Once you're inspired, you can order most things you need over the internet: plants, seeds, garden furniture and books. And you can benefit from the experience of gardeners all over the globe, 24 hours a day.

The best sites are dynamic and evolving all the time and are worth bookmarking for regular visits. Information is updated regularly and you will find that the contributors in many cases are well respected gardeners and journalists.

Even on the poorer sites there is quality information to be had. It may just require more perseverance to find it. Very few of the gardening sites provide low calibre information. Some are more basic than others and others may be lacking in design, but bear in mind that in many cases that these are the products of devoted gardeners and that quite often these are where gems, however small, are to be found.

Reviews are written from the point of view of a UK gardener, so sites that are relevant are rated more highly. But it is a fact of life that many of the American sites are better established, slicker and offer more content. The quality of UK sites is catching up fast and I hope in future editions we may see more home-grown contributions.

Much of the information to be gleaned from the US sites is still relevant. All you have to do is work out what Hardiness Zone you're in, since this how American gardeners define what plants will grow where they live. You can find more about hardiness zones on the facing page.

If you can't find the information you're looking for, you can always ask. The Web is host to numerous Forums, chat rooms, FAQs and Newsgroups , all places where gardeners meet in cyberspace. One thing gardeners love almost as much as tilling the soil is sharing their love and knowledge of gardening with their fellow green-fingered friends.

Be prepared to experiment, as although the list of sites reviewed here contains some of the best, it is by no means exhaustive. The field is constantly expanding and sites are evolving all the time. Be confident: click around, follow up links, ask questions and you may find just the information you are looking for. Above all, relax and enjoy yourself: the web is easy, once you know how.

Sue Little, March 2000

Hardiness Zones

Many of the sites covered in this book originate from the United States and it is inevitable that you will come across the terms Hardiness Zones or USDA (short for United States Department of Agriculture) Growing Zones, whilst browsing through the sites.

Because of the climatic diversity there, American gardeners tend to identify themselves by the growing zone they live in. The term 'hardiness' refers to the average annual minimum temperatures experienced in an area, and it provides a guide to how hardy plants need to be to survive in a particular part of the country.

When using US gardening sites, particularly forums, bulletin boards and Q&A sections, you will be able to work out which items and plant recommendations are of most relevance to you if you understand what the zones mean and which zone your garden is in.

The majority of the UK, including South East England, Wales and South West England falls in Zone 9, with a frost hardiness of between 20° to 30° degrees Fahrenheit (-2° to -7° Celsius). Most of the rest of the UK is in Zone 8 (10° to 20° Fahrenheit; -7° to -12° Celsius), apart from very northern parts of Scotland, which fall into Zone 7 (0° to 10° Fahrenheit; -12° to -17° Celsius). The further north you go in the UK the hardier the plants need to be.

For further details or to find a map of the zones for the USA, try sites such as www.ncpmh.org/zones, or for the rest of Europe, we recommend The Swedish Fuchsia Society at www2.dicom.se/fuchsias/eurozoner.html.

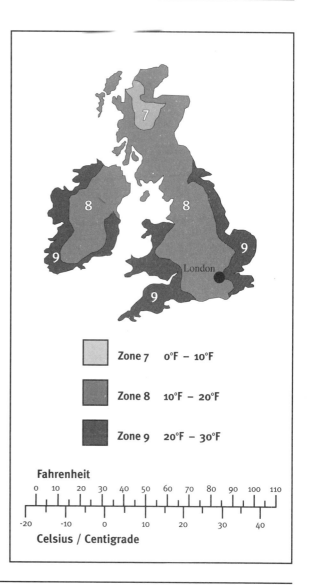

	Zone 7	0°F – 10°F
	Zone 8	10°F – 20°F
	Zone 9	20°F – 30°F

Fahrenheit

0   10   20   30   40   50   60   70   80   90   100   110

-20   -10   0   10   20   30   40

Celsius / Centigrade

Chapter 1

Essential sites

www.rhs.org.uk
The Royal Horticultural Society

Overall rating: ★ ★ ★ ★ ★			
Classification: Society		**Readability:**	★ ★ ★ ★ ★
Updating: Monthly		**Reliability:**	★ ★ ★ ★ ★
Navigation: ★ ★ ★ ★ ★		**Speed:**	★ ★ ★

UK

This is a large, impressive site that works well and looks good. It's packed full of information about the society and includes some useful databases. Information is well laid out and the site is both easy to read and navigate. A central column of text is positioned between a menu tree, which provides access to the other main sections of the site, and icons displaying links to other items. With the exception of the icons leading to the three main databases, the navigation tools remain on the site permanently, making it impossible to get lost whilst looking around. Information is revised monthly, with more frequent updates for news items.

The main disadvantage is its speed and some parts can be slow to download, especially at times when the site is busy. Sunday afternoons are best avoided.

There's a lot to do and see on this exemplary site, although the information tends to be on the theoretical side and there's a disappointing lack of any input about the practical business of gardening. There's also room for improvement in the online shopping pages.

SPECIAL FEATURES
There's a wealth of information which is well-catalogued and easy to find. The homepage is dedicated to garden news, viewpoints and reports. Other features can be found by clicking on the icons or by using the site map.

Help explains how the navigation symbols work (each of the main sections is indicated by a label, which also leads to subsections) and gives a useful introduction to the site.

Search enables you to find specific information quickly. There are three main searchable databases, which are accessed via the pushbuttons at the top of the homepage.

Bookfinder A database which can be searched by author, title or keyword. Entries are accompanied by full bibliographical details and a brief synopsis. Books can be bought online via a link to www.gardeningstore.com.

Plantfinder An online version of the RHS's bestselling book to help you find elusive or unusual plants, with a searchable database listing over 70 000 plants from over 800 UK nurseries. If looking for specific plants you need to be able to tell your species from your genera and cultivars, and it's worth checking spellings offline in advance to avoid frustration. The returns from the search give a list of nurseries stocking the specific plant, with full contact details, and links to their web-sites if they have one. There is plenty of help to make the most of this efficient and useful online resource. The only failing is the inability to search within specific regions, although you can use the Nursery finder to search for selected regional suppliers.

Productfinder This is less satisfactory than the other main databases on the site. A pull-down menu of categories (such as Statuary and Windchimes) gives access to over 2000 suppliers of garden accessories. However, some contact details proved inadequate and the database would be improved with more details about the actual products.

Other Features

Links The list of links to other sites is quite comprehensive and ranges from English Heritage, Forestry Commission, Royal Botanical Gardens at Kew, to bookshops and gardens in the UK and the rest of the world.

About the RHS Introduces the Royal Horticultural Society as it is today and throughout its past, illustrated with photographs and drawings. There are also details on membership, libraries and collections.

Around Britain allows the user to conduct a regional search using a clickable map which reveals details of gardens, nurseries, shows and colleges. Alternatively you can select any of these individual categories to view a general list covering the whole of the UK.

Plant of the Month outlines the history and origins of a named plant and gives information on cultivation, propagation, pests and diseases.

Plants provides information on the various departments of the society, such as Science Departments, Trials and Awards, The Environment (a series of online leaflets on issues such as peat, limestone, and genetic engineering) and Plant Names, where you can make a search of plants in the Wisley collection.

Education gives details of courses, colleges, training, and the work done by the RHS with children at Wisley and in schools.

Publications highlights what's on offer in the RHS shop, including books and journals, from which a selection of articles are available to read online.

This enormous site is probably the best UK online gardening resource, and has a lot to offer British gardeners. This site is a must for serious net gardeners.

www.garden.com

Garden.com

Overall rating: ★ ★ ★ ★ ★		
Classification: Ezine	**Readability:**	★ ★ ★ ★
Updating: Daily	**Reliability:**	★ ★ ★ ★
Navigation: ★ ★ ★ ★ ★	**Speed:**	★ ★ ★

US

A huge amount of searchable information is presented in a well-designed format, and a good balance of text and photos gives it the feel of a quality magazine. Don't be put off by the initially alarming multitude of links. They are necessary for a site with such extensive contents and there is a full listing in each section to ensure that you don't miss anything. The site is updated daily and information is generally reliable, though it concentrates on ideas and inspiration, rather than heavyweight garden knowledge.

DESIGN

Plantfinder Enter the Sun Exposure and the Hardiness Zone (see p.11) of your garden and this feature proffers a list of plants which are suitable, and for US browsers, available to buy.

Garden Planner An excellent online resource which allows you to download free garden design software, as well as providing advice on choosing suitable plants.

Designs and Collections A selection of plant collections and garden layouts which are ready to use. Of more use to gardeners in the US.

Design Portfolio An archive of past design features from the magazine for inspiration.

OUR COMMUNITY

Chat/Celebrity chat An easy-to-use and popular feature which allows you to converse with gardeners around the globe. There are also weekly chats with celebrity gardeners.

Garden Doctor An opportunity to ask a question or search the database for previously-answered questions. This works best by keeping keywords brief and then browsing the results.

Gardener's forum Take a look at what other gardeners are doing or showcase your own efforts by sending in a photo and brief description.

Other features in this section include **Send a Postcard, Quiz of the Week** and **Kid's Gardening Camp.**

Other sections

Magazine contains a series of features, such as Weekend Projects, Garden of the Month, Gardening Basics, and Plant Profiles. Items such as Kitchen Gardening provide plenty of tips on how to consume fresh garden produce and you can encourage wildlife into the garden with advice from Nature's Garden.

The monthly contents of each issue can be viewed using Article Search and the Glossary provides useful and extensive help with gardening terms.

Shop is for US readers only.

Membership is easy and free, and makes return visits to the site more worthwhile. As a member you can design and save multiple gardens on the design software, personalise the site for yourself, receive an e-newsletter, and freely use the garden doctor service.

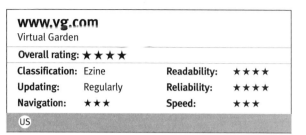

www.vg.com
Virtual Garden

Overall rating: ★ ★ ★ ★			
Classification: Ezine		**Readability:**	★ ★ ★ ★
Updating: Regularly		**Reliability:**	★ ★ ★ ★
Navigation: ★ ★ ★		**Speed:**	★ ★ ★
US			

Although some parts of this very large and rambling site are very much US-focused, there is plenty to interest UK gardeners, although it can be difficult to find. Navigation can be tricky, but there is a useful site map and the menu bar will always point you in the right direction. Generally the pages are well-laid out and easily readable but links are slow and articles take some time to download, which can be tiresome. The contents are up to date and generally reliable. Many of the gardening writers are specialists in a particular area. Be aware that this site appears to make subtle changes to its format occasionally, and new sections appear.

TOOLSHED
This should probably be your first port of call. It concentrates on the practicalities of using the site.

The Time Life Plant Encyclopedia is a database of over 3000 species, which can be tracked down by name, keyword, or attribute, such as size, colour, season of interest.

VG Vine gives information on the Virtual Garden club, and in particular the email newsletter that members receive.

Dig the Net allows you to search the web for garden-related topics.

Search this Site is probably the most efficient way to use the site. Specific areas of the site can be reached or a subject can be searched by keyword.

WHAT'S NEW
This section aims to keep the visitor up to date with site developments and more general gardening news.

On the Newsstand offers synopses of the best articles in this month's US gardening magazines.

News You Can Use provides links to seasonal articles from the previous year.

HOW-TO RESOURCES
This is the main source of article-based information.

VG Library has lots of information from past editions of VG. You can browse articles written by particular authors, or click on Outdoor Living for a more general index of garden-related subjects.

Gardening with Kids is an extensive area offering lots of ideas for projects, tips and ideas for sharing the garden with children.

OTHER SECTIONS
Regional Gardener is mostly of interest to the US gardener, but if you know which zone your garden falls within (see p. 11), you may well find some useful information here.

Gardener's World is a compendium of useful link headings which may be of interest to UK residents, organised under the headings Botanic Gardens, Plant Societies and Books.

Let's Talk Dirt accesses the many VG forums. You must be a member to post messages, but can browse the replies freely.

About VG, Gardening Basics, Landscaping and Lawns and Weekend Projects are also worth a look.

Lots of interest for UK gardeners, although it can sometimes be tricky to find.

www.e-garden.co.uk
E-Garden

Overall rating: ★ ★ ★ ★			
Classification: Ezine		**Readability:**	★ ★ ★ ★
Updating: Monthly		**Reliability:**	★ ★ ★ ★ ★
Navigation: ★ ★ ★		**Speed:**	★ ★

UK

A fairly new site making a good impression so far, and improving as the archives begin to fill up. Richard Jackson, gardening correspondent for *News of the World* and presenter of ITV's *Grassroots* and Geoff Hodge, gardening editor of *Garden Answers* are the main writers. Information is generally well-maintained and revised monthly. However due to the age of the site (still in its infancy at the time of writing) some of the links still need attention and pages can take a long time to download.

SPECIAL FEATURES

Garden Answers Richard and Geoff provide advice via email, to gardener's queries. Response times are good and answers are comprehensive, listing suppliers and planting ideas as appropriate.

Seasonal Plants A suggested list of plants for each month of the year which perform well and are easily available at garden centres.

Seasonal Tips Tips for the month outlining jobs to do, listed under different headings, for example Kitchen Garden, Houseplants, Lawn Care.

Seasonal Projects Archived articles on a selection of seasonal topics.

Out and About A few suggestions of topically-relevant jobs to be doing in the garden.

Features More information on a few selected subjects.

Buy it Online A few special offers and a selection of reviewed books.

This site is improving all the time, and it's certainly worth a look for the new gardener.

www.suite101.com/category.cfm/gardening
Suite 101

Overall rating: ★ ★ ★ ★

Classification:	Ezine	**Readability:**	★ ★ ★ ★
Updating:	Monthly	**Reliability:**	★ ★ ★ ★
Navigation:	★ ★ ★ ★	**Speed:**	★ ★ ★

US

This is one of 800 sites hosted by Suite 101, each on a different topic. The Gardening site consists of over 60 separate subject pages, making this site an excellent resource for finding out more about almost any area of gardening. Each page has its own Editor, selected for their particular expertise. New articles are posted every month and information is constantly added to the discussion boards, which are always open.

Moving around each site section is easy since there's a permanent tool bar and navigation buttons, though at times the pages can be a little slow to download.

SPECIAL FEATURES

This site covers a huge range of gardening, including Cottage Gardening, Organic Gardening, Container Gardening, Kids Gardens, and English Town Gardening, with each area subdivided into three main sections:

Articles Written by the editor, these are always pertinent and based on personal experience. They are changed monthly and archived by date.

Discussions There is a discussion board for each subject, some better-used than others.

Links The top five websites for each subject are listed and reviewed, and there's a substantial list of other relevant sites.

Most people will find something of interest here.

Chapter 2

Your Garden

Design and Planning

Probably because garden designers work on a commercial basis, there aren't many sites dedicated to offering free design advice, but these two sites have practical and inspirational content, and you'll also find ideas from many of the magazines and larger sites.

www.teleport.com/~lengstro/index.html			
Garden Aesthetics			
Overall rating: ★ ★ ★			
Classification:	Homepage	Readability:	★ ★ ★
Updating:	Monthly	Reliability:	★ ★ ★ ★
Navigation:	★ ★ ★	Speed:	★ ★ ★ ★

US

This is the site of Linda Engstrom, a garden designer from Oregon with over 25 years of experience in garden design. Her passion and speciality is creating individual gardens with a unique sense of place. Although the site's primary function is to advertise Ms Engstrom's work, there is still useful information for would-be landscape gardeners and it's very good for those interested in the classical principles of design from a practical perspective.

Some of the pages can be text-heavy and it may be easier to download or print pages to read at leisure.

SPECIAL FEATURES
Genus Loci Photos and descriptions of Ms.Engstrom's beautifully-designed garden. There are more, seasonal reports in the 'Photo Gallery'.

Garden Making A comprehensive resource with many ideas for design based on the principles of line, form, texture, and colour.

Structures Help and advice, with photos, for how to best use structures in your garden.

Featured Design Photos and explanations of recently undertaken garden designs.

Garden Tours Illustrated reports on garden visits from a designer's perspective.

www.arts.monash.edu.au/visarts/diva/gardens.html		
Gardens and Landscape Design		
Overall rating: ★ ★ ★		
Classification: Academic	**Readability:**	★ ★ ★
Updating: Unclear	**Reliability:**	★ ★ ★ ★
Navigation: ★ ★ ★	**Speed:**	★ ★ ★ ★
AUS		

Just click on the gardens you want to see for inspirational images from the Visual Arts library of Monash University, Victoria, Australia. The selection of good quality, digital images are from the historic gardens of nine Italian villas and Monet's garden in Giverny. A very pleasant and peaceful diversion.

OTHER SITES OF INTEREST

Garden.Com
www.garden.com
The Garden.com site contains 3 sections which will be of use to the budding garden designer. The Garden Planner allows you to download free design software, as well as providing advice on choosing suitable plants. There's also an archive of past design features and a selection of plant collections and garden layouts which are ready for use.

Archived and searchable articles

These pages make excellent use of the web's resources, enabling you to search for and download articles on almost any topic. Many of the sites specialise in one or more subjects, or organise the articles by subject matter. If you don't find what you're looking for here, try searching some of the magazine sites, which by their nature are mostly article-based.

www.urbanext.uiuc.edu/hort/index.html
Hort Corner

Overall rating: ★ ★ ★ ★ ★			
Classification: Academic		**Readability:**	★ ★ ★ ★
Updating: Monthly		**Reliability:**	★ ★ ★ ★ ★
Navigation: ★ ★ ★ ★		**Speed:**	★ ★ ★ ★

US

The University of Illinois offers masses of information about gardening and horticulture, and most of it is gathered here in this huge but easy-to-use resource. All the information within the site can be trusted and is updated once a month. There is a great deal of interest here to UK gardeners, especially for those who are less experienced, although it is worth remembering that it is intended to be relevant to the state of Illinois. (See Hardiness Zones map, p. 11).

The site is careful to provide return links, making navigation simple. Text is also clear and straightforward, though more photos would add visual interest.

SPECIAL FEATURES
Hort Corner acts as a portal to other sites hosted by the University of Illinois, some of which are permanent, others seasonal and each with its own speciality. They all include a number of reliable and informative articles. Those of particular interest include:

Our Rose Garden A good source of information on the history of roses, as well as choosing, planting, caring for, and pruning them.

Apples and More Full of fascinating history and legends, and facts on varieties, nutrition and cultivation.

Watch Your Garden Grow Dedicated to growing, storing,

and preparing vegetables of many different types, with advice on choosing varieties, planting, care, and problem solving.

Bulbs and More   Gives a scholarly introduction to the biology of the bulb, and goes on to cover history, planting tips, use in design, indoor bulbs, and FAQs.

Gardening Basics   A good short introduction to essentials like composting, planning, planting, and growing vegetables and herbs.

The Master Gardener Gazette is a sister website of Hort Corner, which lists the contents of back issues and includes a surprisingly large and useful section called Hort Shorts. These cover an enormous range of subject matter, from seasonal tips to wildflowers to kitchen gardening. It can be found at:

www.urbanext.uiuc.edu/peoria/gazette/index.html

All the garden-related information on each site may be searched using the very efficient search-by-keyword facility.

A reliable source of information for the less experienced gardener and well worth the time spent browsing.

www.windowbox.com
Windowbox

Overall rating: ★★★★★			
Classification:	Ezine	**Readability:**	★★★★★
Updating:	Weekly	**Reliability:**	★★★★
Navigation:	★★★★★	**Speed:**	★★★★★
US			

Intelligence and wit are combined in this innovative site to produce a rare thing: a website that is creative, entertaining and packed with knowledge. Biographical details of the contributors are listed in The Experts section, along with their qualifications. It's easy to read and is well laid out with some quirky illustrations, and obvious links make browsing around very simple. Inevitably some features are only for the US, but this site is definitely worth a look. A Californian site devoted to getting the most out of container gardening , anywhere. It has a strong community feel and is committed to encouraging urban gardening.

SPECIAL FEATURES

The Floracle asks you several questions about your climate, your garden, the sizes and types of plants you want to use and your dedication to their welfare. It then offers a list of suitable plants, both annuals and perennials, with more details and cultivation hints if you click. It's not really designed for UK users, since it's necessary to indicate a zip code, but the site and recommended typing in 27601 which loosely covers the climate here. It gives some great ideas for unusual, beautiful, and edible plants.

Terrace Times flags up what's new on the site, with quick links to the latest gardening articles, and an archived list of previous features, of which there are a fair number.

The Experts is a uniquely original feature written in a quirkily retro style. Four fictional experts, each with a hilarious and captivating personal biography, specialise in a particular area of container gardening. Their main subject areas are clickable and lead to a substantial list of short topical articles, and there is also a quick tip.

Dr Botnic PhD looks at the science of plants in The basics of botany, Understanding your microclimate, and Choosing containers.

The Care Counsellor helps to nurture good relationships with your plants in Watering - it's trickier than you think, Feeding, The Forces of Evil, and Propagation and other intimaciea.

The Design Queen gives advice on planning and designing your garden: Planning your garden, Placing containers, Planting a harmonious container and Selecting plants.

Chef Clive looks at the productive container garden in Using herbs and flowers, Entertaining on your balcony, and Making your balcony a private haven.

A real novelty. This site aims to inform and entertain and does both successfully.

www.gardening.about.com
About.com guide to Gardening

Overall rating: ★ ★ ★ ★

Classification:	Ezine	Readability:	★ ★ ★ ★
Updating:	Fortnightly	Reliability:	★ ★ ★
Navigation:	★ ★ ★ ★	Speed:	★ ★ ★

US

The About.com guide to gardening is part of a network of sites, which provide expert advice on a variety of subjects. In this case Deborah Simpson, a landscape gardener and designer is the site's resident expert. Much of the site is aimed at the US, but information relevant to the UK can be obtained if you know your hardiness zones. (See p. 11). Other aspects of the site are reviewed in Link Sites, p. 120.

SPECIAL FEATURES

Articles displays nearly 100 features from the last three years either by date, or by topic which is easier to use.

Netlinks is a fairly comprehensive resource of garden-related websites and About.com articles, sorted into groups and listed alphabetically. When these links are followed an About.com toolbar floats above, making it easy to return to the main site.

Search offers the facility to search the site or the whole of About.com.

Related has links to other About.com pages which may be of interest.

Share this site allows you to email pages to a friend.

A useful resource and a good place to start if you're looking for specific information.

www.which.net/gardening/contents.html
Which? Online

Overall rating: ★ ★ ★ ★

Classification:	Ezine	Readability:	★ ★ ★ ★
Updating:	Monthly	Reliability:	★ ★ ★ ★ ★
Navigation:	★ ★ ★	Speed:	★ ★ ★ ★

UK £ R

A substantial amount of knowledgeable advice and honest appraisal is available from the Which? site, and as ever the information is of the highest calibre. However, it is at a price and at the time of writing a subscription covering the entire Which? site cost £7.75 per month. Each month you can read an in-depth article for free, but you need to subscribe to access the bulk of the site. It's easy enough to move around the main site if you're nimble with the mouse, but navigating the forums can be hairy as information is not immediately obvious.

SPECIAL FEATURES

Monthly Reports covers a wide range of gardening topics in some depth. These include Design Ideas, Planting Suggestions, Plant Profiles and Trials.There are between ten and fifteen articles each month in an archive which dates back two years.

Factsheets are organised into three categories: How to covers the basics in a step-by-step format; Expert explores subjects in depth and Troubleshooting answers FAQs on a wide range of pest and disease problems.

There's a lot here, but the price may exlude some and a bit of detective work might reveal the answers elsewhere for free.

www.gardenguides.com
Garden Guides

Overall rating: ★ ★ ★ ★

Classification:	Ezine	Readability:	★ ★ ★ ★
Updating:	Monthly	Reliability:	★ ★ ★ ★
Navigation:	★ ★ ★	Speed:	★ ★ ★

US

Comprehensive and reliable information is presented in a format designed to make online reading easy at this site, which has excellent photos and well-laid-out text. Despite this though, the homepage is confusing and to see the range of material available it's best to click on Browse Articles. There is an extensive range of articles, which cover subjects as diverse as 'encouraging beneficial insects', to 'producing herbal hair tonics'. Some are in the form of personal stories, whilst others are more academic in style, but all are undoubtedly informative, and accompanied by a short but pertinent biography of the author.

SPECIAL FEATURES

All articles are listed in Browse Articles under headings such as Basics, Design, Food from the Garden, Herb Gardening, and Water Gardening. The email address of the author is given, making feedback possible.

This site is especially useful for beginners needing advice, and those with a developing interest in gardening.

www.thegardenhelper.com/gardenerindex.html
The Garden Helper

Overall rating: ★ ★ ★			
Classification: Homepage		**Readability:**	★ ★ ★ ★
Updating: Monthly		**Reliability:**	★ ★ ★ ★
Navigation: ★ ★ ★ ★		**Speed:**	★ ★ ★ ★

UK

www.naturalland.com/gv.htm
Natural Land Gardening Village

Overall rating: ★ ★ ★			
Classification: Information		**Readability:**	★ ★ ★ ★
Updating: Weekly		**Reliability:**	★ ★ ★ ★
Navigation: ★ ★ ★ ★		**Speed:**	★ ★ ★ ★

UK

An enormous, rambling personal site, which is updated every month, and contains some informative gardening articles of interest to the beginner. The range of articles appears to be random, but a list of the latest additions appears on the homepage, so it doesn't take long to see if anything takes your fancy.

It's easy to get lost here but that's part of the experience, if you don't mind finding out about 1950s rock music by mistake as well.

Browse down the main page to find the various different ways of accessing the information. There are articles on general gardening, annuals, perennials and bulbs, fruit and veg, pests, and a glossary.

This site is of particular interest to anyone with an interest in health and is one of a number of Villages which cover related subjects such as organic food, herbs and nutrition. As yet the number of articles available is quite small, but the authors are experienced and well qualified, and news stories are updated weekly. Utilising the Gardening Village Home button, or any of the links at the bottom of the page makes navigation straightforward.

SPECIAL FEATURES

The articles are archived into Departments, found on the right hand side of the page.

Tips and techniques covers gardening basics such as organic pest control and planning your garden.

Blooming Gardens explores plant-related subjects like naturalising bulbs and choosing scented roses.

The Tool Shed gives advice on choosing the right tool.

Fresh Food Gardening offers articles on growing different varieties of fruit and veg.

The Herb Gardener profiles a selection of herbs, giving uses and tips for cultivation.

Of special interest to those with a leaning towards alternative health.

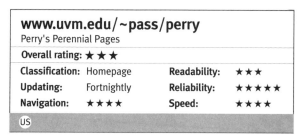

www.uvm.edu/~pass/perry

Perry's Perennial Pages

Overall rating: ★ ★ ★			
Classification:	Homepage	**Readability:**	★ ★ ★
Updating:	Fortnightly	**Reliability:**	★ ★ ★ ★ ★
Navigation:	★ ★ ★ ★	**Speed:**	★ ★ ★ ★

US

The eponymous Dr Perry is a professor in plant and soil science at the University of Vermont, and this site provides masses of information on choosing and growing perennial plants, with articles frequently being added to the list. Looking around the site is reasonably easy: just scroll down the homepage to select from the main menu and return to the homepage by clicking on the links at the foot of each page. However, the site is very text heavy, and although audiovisual diversions are included on the site, additional software is needed to access them.

Parts of the site require Java for maximum effect. Realplayer G2 (downloadable) is needed to access the multimedia welcome files and music on certain pages. Across Lite software (also downloadable) is necessary for the puzzles and crosswords.

SPECIAL FEATURES

FAQs are grouped by general topic category such as What plant and where, Care and culture, What's wrong? and General. There are a large number of questions and answers, and a good deal is relevant to the UK gardener.

For the Home Gardener is a resource base and includes leaflets, articles, radio programmes, and slide shows. Much is local to Eastern USA but there is also plenty of general information such as garden colour, designing with perennials, and the best use of the internet for gardeners.

Perennial Arcade has a number of puzzles and quizzes on the subject of garden plants.

There's a lot of information here but it needs careful sifting. You don't need all the software to appreciate the site: it bears up without the gimmicks.

Getting Help - Advice and Problem Solving

If you're struggling with a really thorny gardening problem, there are specialist experts of every kind out there, just waiting for you to contact them. These are the best services available, plus a couple of resources on everyone's most hated gastropod: the slug.

www.allexperts.com
Allexperts

Overall rating: ★ ★ ★ ★			
Classification:	Information	**Readability:**	★ ★
Updating:	Unclear	**Reliability:**	★ ★ ★ ★
Navigation:	★ ★	**Speed:**	★ ★ ★ ★

UK

Gardening is just one of the many topics to be found at the Allexperts website. It provides a free Question and Answer service, which operates via email.

The Gardening section can be found under the Arts and Entertainments heading on the homepage, and offers expert advice on a number of topics. First choose the topic, and then select your advisor from a list of three or four experts. A short biography of each expert is available, to help make your choice, in addition to ranking for each of their skills such as knowledge, clarity of advice and politeness. The availability of each expert is also listed. The site promises that 50 per cent of questions will be answered in 24 hours and the speed of answers to test questions bore this out. They were also thorough and well thought-out, and a good number of possible solutions were given.

Moving around the site is quick, though it's easy to be distracted by the large menu bar, which sits permanently at the top of the page, and the animated banner ad. Keep in mind that information always starts under the menu bar, and you will usually have to scroll down to make it accessible.

www.igarden.co.uk
Igarden

Overall rating: ★ ★ ★ ★			
Classification:	Ezine	**Readability:**	★ ★ ★ ★
Updating:	Unclear	**Reliability:**	★ ★ ★ ★
Navigation:	★ ★ ★ ★	**Speed:**	★ ★ ★

UK

www.garden.org
National Gardening Association (US)

Overall rating: ★ ★ ★			
Classification:	Information	**Readability:**	★ ★
Updating:	Frequently	**Reliability:**	★ ★ ★ ★
Navigation:	★ ★	**Speed:**	★ ★ ★

US

This comprehensive online magazine containing a Garden Advice Centre provides an efficient and reliable service. It offers sound and authorative advice, albeit in a less personal manner than some other sites.

Finding your way around is straightforward: scroll down the home page to find a link to the Advice Centre. Options are then presented clearly and moving from page to page is simple.

SPECIAL FEATURES

The Garden Advice Centre offers two options: search a large and comprehensive database of previous responses or email your own question for a personal reply. This service is free, although you need to register as a subscriber to take advantage of it. Our test question was answered efficiently and within 12 hours, although it lacked the personal feel it appears to aim for.

For a review of other aspects of this site, see p. 121.

A 48-hour gardening question and answer service which provides well-thought-out and solid advice. Travelling around the site is fairly quick although it is necessary to follow a link to a sponsor site in order to post your question. An overabundance of frames and some unclear text slow the process down a little.

SPECIAL FEATURES

The question and answer service is the site's most notable feature. You are encouraged to search the **FAQs** first but these provided limited information. If it is relevant to your question, mention that your garden is in Britain.

www.oxalis.co.uk/slug.htm
Slug Control

Overall rating: ★ ★ ★ ★			
Classification:	Homepage	Readability:	★ ★ ★ ★
Updating:	Unclear	Reliability:	★ ★ ★ ★
Navigation:	★ ★ ★	Speed:	★ ★ ★

UK

This site is a godsend for anyone who has ever suffered from a slug-infested garden and is a comprehensive study of slug control by Dr Bill Symondson of the University of Wales. The site is in the form of a single long page, but the content is well formatted and is easily readable.

SPECIAL FEATURES

Slug Identification How to identify whether the slugs in your garden are a danger to your plants, with illustrations of various varieties.

Chemical Slug Control Which chemicals to use for optimum damage to slugs and minimum damage to the garden.

Non Chemical Slug Control Highlights methods such as beer traps and massacre by pointed stick.

Cultivation Garden maintenance to minimise slug populations.

Slug Predators and Parasites Encouraging natural destroyers and reistant plant varieties.

www.powerup.com.au/~swimskins/slug_snail_FAQ.html
Slug and Snail FAQ

Overall rating: ★ ★ ★			
Classification:	Homepage	Readability:	★ ★ ★
Updating:	Unclear	Reliability:	★ ★ ★
Navigation:	★ ★	Speed:	★ ★ ★

AUS

Another hefty piece of research on the best ways to cope with the slimy army, this time by Margaret van Emmerik, an Australian gardener, who has trawled the web and spent hours searching through books in an attempt to collate all the available information. She presents a wealth of creative and quirky ideas for creating barriers and lures and offers a good number of suggestions for collection techniques, including the popular Spot'n'slice and Spot'n'squash.

OTHER SITES OF INTEREST

e-garden
www.e-garden.co.uk
The **Garden Answers** section on this site, with email advice provided by Richard Jackson and Geoff Hamilton, is well worth a look. See p. 19 for the full review.

Kitchen Gardening

Although many of the larger magazine-style sites offer some advice on fruit and vegetable growing, these sites are dedicated to the subject.

www.taunton.com/kg
Kitchen Gardener Online

Overall rating: ★★★★			
Classification:	Ezine	**Readability:**	★★★★
Updating:	Monthly	**Reliability:**	★★★★
Navigation:	★★★★	**Speed:**	★★★

US

This is an online edition of the US print magazine, which has a lot to offer gardeners interested in both cooking and eating. The pages are well-designed, with a vertical band of text and good quality images, though article pages can be slow to download. The button bar at the top of the homepage leads to articles on aspects of kitchen gardening such as Growing, Cooking, Design, Techniques and Projects. The range of articles is eclectic and covers subjects such as storing root crops and using up abundant tomatoes, and all are accompanied by the author's credentials.

SPECIAL FEATURES

Growing, Cooking and **Techniques** are the sections richest in information, with a good number of articles, tips and recipes taken from the print magazine.

Plot Notes is a fairly well-used discussion board where you might well find the answer to a problem or track down rare seed.

A luscious, informative resource for the kitchen gardener, even if it is just ways to use all those courgettes.

http://dialspace.dial.pipex.com/town/ close/xpz05/homepage.htm		
Allotment and Kitchen Gardens		
Overall rating: ★ ★		
Classification: Society	**Readability:**	★ ★
Updating: Monthly	**Reliability:**	★ ★ ★
Navigation: ★ ★	**Speed:**	★ ★ ★
UK		

The homepage of The Barnet Federation of Allotment and Horticultural Societies appears rather muddling at first sight. On the left you will find articles on allotments and allotment life, and on the right there are links to other sites, listed by category. Once you leave the homepage, things are much easier, and a navigation bar at the bottom of each page makes the options clear. Reading can be heavy going, though, as the text completely fills the page.

A useful site if you are looking for an allotment or local society in your area, and you can also join the Kitchen Gardens email community.

OTHER SITES OF INTEREST

Garden.com
www.garden.com

Within the Magazine section of this site, you'll find the Kitchen Gardening pages, written and maintained by Renée Shepherd, garden writer and founder of Shepherd's Seeds, a Californian company specialising in gourmet seeds. There are a large number of articles on growing fruit and vegetables, cooking with herbs, and edible flowers. You'll also find a huge number of delicious recipes using garden produce. See also The Essential Sites pp12-19.

Organic Gardening

Organic gardeners are well catered-for on the web, and in fact the large majority of general gardening sites incline themselves at least in part to non-chemical gardening. These are the best sites devoted entirely to the subject.

www.oldgrowth.org/compost
The Compost Resource Page

Overall rating: ★ ★ ★ ★ ★			
Classification:	Homepage	**Readability:**	★ ★ ★ ★ ★
Updating:	Regularly	**Reliability:**	★ ★ ★ ★
Navigation:	★ ★ ★ ★ ★	**Speed:**	★ ★ ★ ★

UK

The Compost Resource Page is a clear, easily readable site, which is intended to be a hub of information for anybody interested in composting. It's an extensive guide covering several areas; including Home Composting, Composting Products and even Compost Poetry. Although the provenance of this site is not stated, information is of the highest calibre and is regularly updated. The contents are well presented and the homepage is clear. Within the different sections of the site, toolbars are located at the top and bottom of each page.

SPECIAL FEATURES

There are two main sources of information: articles provided by the site and links to other similar sites, which can be found by clicking the icons in the centre of the homepage.

General Information contains a massive amount of detail on the basics of composting. There can't be anything anyone needs to know that isn't here.

Home composting covers everything from bin design to articles exploring the scientific principles of compost-making.

Vermi-composting explains all you could want to know about worm bins.

The Composter's Forum hosts an incredible 12 different

forums on compost-related topics. Some are better used than others but we found the general home-composter's forum to be regularly visited and well-used. There are archives available, through which you can search for posts on specific problems.

The most extensive guide to composting found on the web.

www.hdra.org.uk
The Henry Doubleday Research Association

Overall rating: ★ ★ ★ ★			
Classification:	Information	**Readability:**	★ ★ ★ ★
Updating:	Monthly	**Reliability:**	★ ★ ★ ★ ★
Navigation:	★ ★ ★ ★	**Speed:**	★ ★ ★ ★

UK

HDRA is the foremost authority on organic gardening with many years of experience, and describes itself as 'Europe's largest organic organisation'. The emphasis here is on fruit and vegetable cultivation, with plenty of practical, well-thought out advice for both new and seasoned growers. A new factsheet is added every month and press releases are always kept current. Pages are well laid out and manageable, but would benefit from some photos. The easiest way to get around is via the menu bar at the top of each page; clicking on Contents brings up a plan of the entire site.

SPECIAL FEATURES

Grow Your Own offers a wealth of advice for getting started with organic fruit and vegetable growing in the form of factsheets, a list of questions and answers, advice on dealing with pests and diseases, and a guide to keeping on top of seasonal garden tasks.

Advice as well as browsing the factsheets you can email the advisory department for help with a specific problem.

Gardens gives information on the three excellent HDRA display gardens, with visiting details and maps.

Links offers an annotated list of organic sites from all over the world.

www.organic.mcmail.com
Organic-UK

Overall rating: ★ ★ ★			
Classification:	Homepage	**Readability:**	★ ★ ★
Updating:	Monthly	**Reliability:**	★ ★ ★ ★
Navigation:	★ ★ ★ ★	**Speed:**	★ ★ ★ ★

UK £ R

This site aims to de-mystify organic gardening, and is a useful resource for beginners. It is owned by Colin Shaw, who has written articles for the Henry Doubleday Research Association and is qualified in organic gardening.

More photos or diagrams would be useful.

SPECIAL FEATURES

Beginner's Pages offer a series of articles on subjects of interest to the new gardener, such as preparing the ground and crop rotation. Questions are directed to the newly-launched Organic Gardening Email Group.

Gardener's Checklist offers a monthly look at what to be getting on with in your garden, and includes a good number of tips and ideas.

Hints and Tips is full of all kinds of ideas, from saving seed to gardening uses for old plastic bottles.

Grow has a good selection of articles, ideas and resources for the organic grower.

News offers a monthly digest of national and international news stories relevant to organic growing.

www.organicgardening.com
Organic Gardening

Overall rating: ★ ★ ★			
Classification:	Ezine	**Readability:**	★ ★ ★
Updating:	Monthly	**Reliability:**	★ ★ ★
Navigation:	★ ★ ★ ★	**Speed:**	★ ★ ★ ★

US

Online version of the US printed magazine that 'teaches beginners the secrets experts know'. The information available to read online is limited, but the authors are experienced and many have published books on organic gardening.

Use the full site listing at the foot of each page to move around the site.

SPECIAL FEATURES

Organic Gardening Basics has a simple introduction to organic gardening and a small number of articles covering subjects of interest to beginners, such as healthy soil, weed control, and composting. Scroll down the home page and click on the Archive link to see a full list of the articles available to read.

Solutions Online answers reader's questions on a monthly basis and there's the opportunity to post your own.

Though intended to highlight the print magazine, this site is nevertheless a brief but useful guide to organic gardening.

www.cat.org.uk
Centre for Alternative Technology

Overall rating: ★ ★ ★			
Classification: Homepage		**Readability:**	★ ★ ★
Updating: Unclear		**Reliability:**	★ ★ ★ ★
Navigation: ★ ★ ★		**Speed:**	★ ★ ★ ★

UK

A good starting point if your interest in organic gardening extends to a sustainable lifestyle. The centre is well-established and is a reliable source on almost any aspect of organic gardening and sustainable living. There's lots of information available on energy conservation, compost-making and other important aspects of gardening organically. Click on the spinning logo to return home from anywhere on the site.

This is a useful resource for anyone interested in an environmentally friendly lifestyle and related gardening subjects.

SPECIAL FEATURES

The Shop has a number of publications on the logistics of organic gardening and the Services section offers help, advice and information on courses at the centre.

The Online Tour works less well, which is a shame. But the centre itself is well worth a visit, and there are details on location, opening times, and what to see.

OTHER SITES OF INTEREST

Companion Plants
www.hitech.net.au/utegrrl/table.htm

A neat one-page site on the practice of using companion plants. There are several tables on the site that inform the grower which plants complement and antagonise one another, and which plants deter potential pests.

Chapter 3

Armchair Gardening

Magazines

In the United States it's common for print magazines to have a web-presence, either the simple presentation of information from the paper edition in a web-page format, or the creation of a more sophisticated, interactive site. With the exception of Plants, all these sites originate from the US, and there's an eclectic mix of styles and formats, although words and (sometimes) pictures are still the basic product.

www.bhg.com/gardening
Better Homes and Gardens

Overall rating: ★ ★ ★ ★

Classification: Magazine		**Readability:**	★ ★
Updating:	Daily	**Reliability:**	★ ★ ★
Navigation:	★ ★	**Speed:**	★ ★ ★ ★

US

Lots of interaction is possible on this site, which is well thought-out and satisfyingly interactive. Although it's more of a pleasant diversion than a serious source of information, it's a must for the serious armchair gardener. Much of the information comes from readers but is well-monitored and the editorial is trustworthy, with fresh material added daily.

In general, it's best to ignore the navigation tree on the left and advertising column on the right: all the relevant information is in the middle column. Watch out for a few duplicate links, and don't be put off by the home page, which lacks focus.

SPECIAL FEATURES

Question of the Week changes every Tuesday. Readers are invited to post their own responses, which are collated and displayed. Several questions are open for comment at any one time, and subject matter is varied, covering topics like 'Pest Control', 'Best Plants for Shade', and popular choices for 'Plant Combinations'.

The BH&G Test Garden is a relatively new feature which looks promising. Photos and features monitor progress so far, projects, planting schemes, and a preview of what's planned for next season.

Other worthwhile elements include a section on **Planning**

and Planting, with suggested designs and planting plans for difficult areas, **Videos** to download on landscaping projects, and three well-used forums on **Indoor and Outdoor Gardening and Advice.**

At first glance this site appears fairly straightforward, but it does offer a few unusual features which don't seem to be duplicated elsewhere.

www.taunton.com/fg
Fine Gardening Online

Overall rating: ★ ★ ★ ★			
Classification: Magazine		**Readability:**	★ ★ ★ ★
Updating: Weekly		**Reliability:**	★ ★ ★
Navigation: ★ ★ ★		**Speed:**	★ ★ ★ ★

US

Online version of the bi-monthly US print magazine which aims to be both useful and inspirational. As you'd expect, this site does a great advertising job for the print edition, but there's still a lot here for free. The site gives no background information on its authors but the advice given is sound, and revised every week.

Pages are a good size and text is easy to read on a white central column with a green background, but moving around the site requires some effort at times and there appear to be one or two broken links.

SPECIAL FEATURES
The links on the main menu bar lead to four different subject areas: **Design, Techniques, Plants,** and **Structures.** Each one contains a number of articles from the print magazine, alphabetically listed under title. There's no indication of the length, which varies considerably, until you download the article, but several run to more than one page. **Design** and **Plants** were found to be the most useful sections, with excellent articles on topics such as 'Aggressive propagation', 'A great garden in just one year', and 'Plants for knot gardens'.

www.traditionalgardening.com
Traditional Gardening

Overall rating: ★ ★ ★ ★			
Classification:	Magazine	**Readability:**	★ ★ ★ ★ ★
Updating:	Quarterly	**Reliability:**	★ ★ ★ ★
Navigation:	★ ★ ★ ★	**Speed:**	★ ★ ★ ★

US

This small but delightful site, with well chosen text and illustrations is a pleasure to read. It is the online version of the US print magazine of the same name and the editor, Michael Weishan, is a US radio broadcaster and author of The New Traditional Garden.

SPECIAL FEATURES

The magazine aims to give practical information on creating and restoring 'classic' gardens, which it successfully does in a gentle, elegant fashion, illustrated throughout with delicate line drawings.

The Current Issue and **Archives** contain the bulk of the information available online. The contents of each print edition are described in full and around three or four articles per edition are downloadable to read online. Subject matter is varied but concentrates on the history of plants and their cultivation, design, and practical instruction on creating an elegant garden with a historical feel.

www.berkeleyhort.com/bhn.htm
Berkeley Horticultural Nursery

Overall rating: ★ ★ ★			
Classification:	Magazine	**Readability:**	★ ★ ★
Updating:	Bi-monthly	**Reliability:**	★ ★ ★ ★
Navigation:	★ ★ ★ ★	**Speed:**	★ ★ ★ ★

US

At first sight this appears to be a factual journal of a purely scientific nature, but it soon reveals itself as a warm, witty online text mag with lots of informative articles, a positive, Californian philosophy and clear, easily readable text. Go straight to Special Features on the homepage as the nursery information is only of interest to those in the San Fransisco area of California.

SPECIAL FEATURES

All articles featured on this website are taken from the print newsletter, *Gardening Suggestions* and can be found under the **Newsletter** section, where they are filed chronologically, or one of the other sections where they are filed according to subject: **Ask Dr Chorophyll, Plant Information, Confronting the Bad Guys,** and **All about Roses**.

www.gardener.women.com/clg
Country Living Gardener

Overall rating: ★ ★ ★			
Classification: Magazine		**Readability:**	★ ★
Updating: Daily		**Reliability:**	★ ★ ★
Navigation: ★ ★ ★		**Speed:**	★ ★

UK

This is the Web page of the US gardening mag, and the sister site of the publications Bloom, Botanica and Homes and Gardens. It's reasonably easy to look around the site; just click on the title bar of each section to view the contents within, and the CLG Header to return to the homepage. The quickest way to find information is to use the search facility, but bear in mind that the site is linked to its sister sites, and once there it's easy to get lost.

SPECIAL FEATURES

There's quite a lot of worthwhile information here, but the trick is finding it.

Inspiration is devoted to ideas for design and increasing garden knowledge. It contains In the Field, plant and garden-related articles, Design contains ideas with video tutorials, Garden Tours of reader's gardens, and Plant Portraits which focuses on a plant or plant family. Note that in order to view the video tutorials you'll need RealMedia or Quicktime software.

Perspiration focuses on the how and when of gardening. Expert Advice gives answers to submitted queries, and the two other sections, Techniques and Sundial provide hints on seasonal jobs and practical projects.

Conversation offers a number of forums for sharing gardening experience. Staff Journals consists of monthly articles by contributing editors, and Your Garden is a place for light-hearted testimony. It's also possible to post a message on one of the messageboards, but we found them to be under-used.

www.digmagazine.com
Dig Magazine

Overall rating: ★ ★ ★

Classification:	Magazine	Readability:	★
Updating:	Regularly	Reliability:	★ ★ ★ ★
Navigation:	★ ★	Speed:	★ ★ ★

US

A strange site with rather an eclectic style, and a lot of information on a huge range of subjects, some of which are unrelated to gardening. There's also a lot of advertising, but it's a treat to find the articles, of which there are nearly 300 written by internationally acclaimed gardeners.

The sheer volume of material can make things frustratingly difficult to find at first, although it's easy when you know how: on the homepage, click on 'Outside', then use the menu on the far left to navigate through the articles.

SPECIAL FEATURES

Articles are listed by category and can be found under one of the following headings: **Design**, **Maintenance**, **Perennials**, **Techniques** and **Resources**.

There are some quality articles to be read here, if you can find your way through the excess information.

www.gardengatemag.com
Garden Gate Magazine

Overall rating: ★ ★ ★

Classification:	Magazine	Readability:	★ ★ ★
Updating:	Bi-monthly	Reliability:	★ ★ ★
Navigation:	★ ★ ★	Speed:	★ ★ ★ ★

US

This is an interesting read if you've got the time to browse, and the site contains a number of practical articles and advice on planning and maintaining a garden. Visually, the homepage is rather busy, but the linked pages are easy to read and follow. There's no information on the writers, but the print magazine has a good following in the US.

SPECIAL FEATURES

Articles are listed under three main headings on the home page: **Garden Tips**, **How-to Articles**, and **Design Articles**. Each contains a fair selection of features, mostly illustrated. You can subscribe to the magazine too.

www.hortmag.com
Horticulture Online

Overall rating: ★ ★ ★			
Classification:	Magazine	**Readability:**	★ ★ ★ ★
Updating:	Bi-monthly	**Reliability:**	★ ★ ★ ★ ★
Navigation:	★ ★ ★	**Speed:**	★ ★ ★

US R

A fairly pedestrian site but one with a good pedigree, since Horticulture is the longest-running gardening magazine in the US with a first class editorial team totalling many years of experience. There is a database of well-illustrated articles from five years worth of the magazine which cover ideas, inspiration and information. All are worth a browse. Navigation is straightforward, but bear in mind that this site contains links to garden.com which can make it difficult if you move from site to site. Registration is tricky and returned a member name and password unrelated to those submitted, but is necessary to read the back issues.

SPECIAL FEATURES

Breaking Ground is where the fun starts, but you need Java to take advantage. It should download in less than 2 minutes, and you need browser versions of 3.0 or later.

From the Magazine is of most interest to UK readers, and in fact most other pages on the site are links to the facilities of garden.com (see p.16) for example, the Garden Planner, Plant Finder and Shopping Section. Registration with this site automatically registers you with garden.com.

Use the **Magazine** section to search a large number of back issues for articles by subject, author, or past issue. The **Gardener's Resources** section provides a large number of links, and some reviews of books and sites.

www.plants-magazine.com
Plants Magazine

Overall rating: ★ ★ ★			
Classification:	Magazine	**Readability:**	★ ★ ★ ★
Updating:	Weekly	**Reliability:**	★ ★ ★ ★ ★
Navigation:	★ ★ ★	**Speed:**	★ ★ ★ ★ ★

UK

This website of the quarterly print magazine is popular with keen gardeners, nursery owners and gardeners with an interest in new and unusual plants. The author is Dirk van der Werff, champion of plant development. If you've discovered or bred a new plant this is the place to publicise it to the community of plant enthusiasts worldwide.

The main menu and latest features can be found by scrolling down the homepage. Once in the different sections you can use the return links to get back to the homepage, though these can be somewhat hit and miss. Information is fascinating and well-illustrated, and it will whet your appetite for the print magazine. Various sections of the site are updated weekly, monthly and quarterly, and you can register to be informed by email when the homepage is updated.

SPECIAL FEATURES

Most interesting and accessible is **Plant of the Week** and the associated **Archives**, which provide in-depth information about the origins and characteristics of specific plants. Descriptions are accompanied by a photograph, and kept well up to date.

Back issues lists the contents of each quarterly issue of the print magazine, and some articles from the earlier issues are available to read on screen.

E-Newsletter allows you to sign up to receive excerpts from the latest magazine, and information on new garden plants.

Nurseryman's Notes by Mike Tristam, details new developments at Binstead Nursery who are leaders in new plant introductions.

www.gardenweb.com/cyberplt
The Cyber-Plantsman

Overall rating: ★ ★ ★			
Classification:	Homepage	**Readability:**	★ ★ ★ ★
Updating:	Occasionally	**Reliability:**	★ ★ ★ ★
Navigation:	★ ★ ★	**Speed:**	★ ★ ★ ★

US

An off-shoot from GardenWeb which focuses on unusual and underused plants. The author has gardened for many years and owns a nursery specialising in unusual plants. Directions around the site can be hit-and-miss; it's best to use the back button on your browser to avoid being directed back to the GardenWeb main site.

SPECIAL FEATURES

The site houses collections of articles submitted by readers or penned by the site's owner. The main sections are Underused Plants, a brief guide to some less well-known varieties, and Plant People, a fascinating glimpse into the life and work of selected champions of unusual plants and plant hunters both dead and alive.

Personal Sites

There are thousands of personal gardening sites owned and maintained by individuals from all over the globe. Each one is a labour of love, with photos, journals, or descriptions of the owner's garden. Visual style and site structure vary tremendously in these pages, but there's always an enormous amount of experience and wisdom. Here are some of the best.

http://www.clubi.ie/dillongarden/
The Dillon Garden

Overall rating: ★ ★ ★ ★ ★				
Classification:	Homepage	**Readability:**		★ ★ ★ ★ ★
Updating:	Bi-monthly	**Reliability:**		★ ★ ★ ★ ★
Navigation:	★ ★ ★ ★ ★	**Speed:**		★ ★ ★ ★

IRE

Helen Dillon, gardening writer and television personality provides a guided tour of her own garden in Dublin and an opportunity for keen gardeners and plant-a-holics to wallow in seductive, inspirational plant descriptions leavened with an earthy humour borne of years of experience. A fair amount of prior knowledge is assumed and the site is more a stimulus to the imagination of existing gardeners than a how-to guide for beginners. Helen Dillon, her garden and her website come across as earthy, good-humoured and seductive. Obviously a real plantswoman, she oozes enthusiasm and the site inspires confidence and is like picking up a good gardening magazine. It's well laid-out and navigation is self-explanatory. The homepage offers a clear contents list and you can also move directly to any option once you have left the homepage by means of a vertical tab down the left hand side of each page. When moving around the site there are useful Back, Next and More buttons. The text is specifically chosen to download quickly and accurately and to be easily readable. It's quicker on pages that are less graphic intensive, although images are used sparingly, with just a few good quality, high-resolution photographs.

SPECIAL FEATURES
The site's focus is Helen Dillon's own garden in Dublin. There is also information about Ms Dillon, and opportunities to buy her books.

The main menu offers the following options:

The Garden A series of excerpts from Helen Dillon's book, An Irish Garden, describing the design history and planting strategy of her own garden. Combines an obvious passion for plants with an honest account of difficulties experienced.

Interview An in-depth biographical interview, specially commissioned and of interest to any gardener.

Articles Features on Helen Dillon's garden taken from papers such as the Irish Times, Financial Times and the Telegraph, by well-known gardening writers.

Hints and Tips Beautifully written and personal, with an honest appraisal of the author's own garden and details of how tasks were tackled - all with a healthy dose of self-deprecating humour and in a chatty, gardener-to-gardener style. There are tantalising descriptions of good seasonal plants to choose.

Fact File and Location give a map and details about how to visit the garden.

Books by Helen Dillon are listed and reviewed and there are links to online bookshops.

You can also browse the full collection of photos from the site in **Photo Gallery**, download a beautiful photo of the garden as desktop wallpaper, join a mailing list, or sign the Guestbook.

www.geocities.com/RainForest/Vines/8433/contents.html

Postcards from the Hedge

Overall rating: ★ ★ ★ ★ ★			
Classification:	Homepage	**Readability:**	★ ★ ★
Updating:	Unclear	**Reliability:**	★ ★ ★
Navigation:	★ ★ ★ ★ ★	**Speed:**	★ ★ ★ ★ ★

Enthusiastic site with clear text and good pictures, which encourages interaction between budding topiarists. There is also a list of extensive links to other topiary related sites.

SPECIAL FEATURES

History of Topiary How the art came about and what sort of plants were first used.

Pruner's Pics Inspirational pictures of topiary.

Plants List of species suitable for artistic pruning.

Books Topiary related books

Clear text and beautiful illustrations will make you want to reach for the secateurs, and take up the art of topiary.

http://guitarweb.music.duq.edu/LPURSE
The Creative Gardener

Overall rating: ★ ★ ★ ★ ★

Classification:	Homepage	**Readability:**	★ ★ ★ ★
Updating:	Regularly	**Reliability:**	★ ★ ★ ★
Navigation:	★ ★ ★ ★	**Speed:**	★ ★ ★ ★

US

Much of the information here is previously published material from the newsletter of the Pittsburg Civic Garden Center, and as well as being reliable and well written, is presented in a simple site with no gimmicky diversions. It's one of the very nicest personal sites, and is full of inspiration, information, and gorgeous photos.

SPECIAL FEATURES

Richly illustrated with the author's own excellent photographs, this beautiful site showcases a musician's garden in Pennsylvania, USA. The text is warm and intelligent, and muses on the relationship between art and gardening.

Colour in the Garden and **Creative Garden Design** lead to a series of previously published articles, of a good length and with clickable links to illustrations. Subjects covered include the use of annuals, colour combinations, winter colour, and texture.

The Plant Gallery is devoted to describing the many different varieties of roses, daylilies, bulbs and foliage grown in the garden, with many lovely photos.

A Composer's Garden introduces the garden and leads to a photographic tour based on the different colour predominances during each season of the year.

www.daisymoore.com
Daisy Moore

Overall rating: ★ ★ ★ ★

Classification:	Homepage	**Readability:**	★ ★ ★
Updating:	Weekly	**Reliability:**	★ ★ ★ ★
Navigation:	★ ★ ★ ★	**Speed:**	★ ★ ★

CAN

Daisy Moore is a Canadian garden designer, gardening writer and radio presenter, who gives advice to anyone planning a less formal garden. The site is especially helpful during the growing season when information is changed weekly. The plain but straightforward homepage gives a brief introduction to each of the sections. Click on the relevant link to view more information.

SPECIAL FEATURES

Tour Daisy's Garden is a huge feature covering several pages, on how she made and maintains her wildflower garden. **Naturalised Gardening**, or sustainable wildflower gardening, is Daisy's speciality and she provides a good deal of information on how to create and maintain your garden in this way. **Tips** are archived and on a wide variety of subjects.

www.hughesmedia.co.uk/eastgrove

Eastgrove Cottage Garden Nursery

Overall rating: ★★★★		
Classification: Nursery	**Readability:**	★★★★
Updating: Unclear	**Reliability:**	★★★★
Navigation: ★★★	**Speed:**	★★

UK

Tiny but exquisite site showcasing the Eastgrove Cottage Garden Nursery, which has been featured in many gardening publications, and newspapers such as the Times, Telegraph and Country Life. Although the nursery doesn't do mail order this site is worth a visit to view the beautifully illustrated **Gallery**, which features several pictures of the cottage garden. There is also a full list of the plants grown there and if you do decide to plan a visit, there's a detailed location map with opening times.

www.maigold.co.uk

Graham's Paradise Garden

Overall rating: ★★★★		
Classification: Homepage	**Readability:**	★★★
Updating: Weekly	**Reliability:**	★★★
Navigation: ★★★	**Speed:**	★★

UK

An enjoyable tour of a small but delightful town garden is to be found here, and much more besides. With over 20 options on the main menu there's really too much to contemplate in one visit, as the site is slow to download and looking around is made difficult by the bewildering array of links and pages. However, this is one of the best personal sites to be found, especially for browsers with Javascript, who can find more information on plants and wildlife at the foot of each page.

SPECIAL FEATURES

Visual tour of the garden is much the best part of the site (see Garden Introduction, Paradise Tour, and Paradise Views) There's also a quiz, information on container gardening, a message board and chat, as well as links to other sites and sponsors, but these work less well and tend to muddle the options.

A small but well-illustrated and intelligent site, describing the small town garden of Lynda Hallinan, editor of the New Zealand Gardening Journal at Suite 101.

SPECIAL FEATURES

The garden information is organised into groups of favourite plants such as **Flowers, Trees,** and **Native Plants**. Each section, headed by a literary quote, is short but has a lot of warmth and personality.

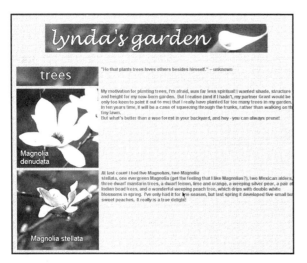

If you're looking for advice on gardening in the shade, then pay a visit to this site, which shares the author's experience of shade-loving plants, plus that of several other related sites. The author is a trained landscape gardener whose interest in shade gardening grew out of necessity, when he acquired a garden dominated by a huge red oak. He modestly claims not to be an expert, but the information provided indicates a great deal of horticultural knowledge.

SPECIAL FEATURES

There's information on the location of the garden and the gardener in question, but the most interesting part is the alphabetical list of plants grown there, each one accompanied by a photo and a personal testimony to its tolerance of shade, flowering habits, and cultivation details.

Some links to other helpful sites are shared, and you can also sign the guestbook or give feedback.

http://darkwing.uoregon.edu/~rbear/garden.html			
A Gardener's Page			
Overall rating: ★ ★ ★			
Classification:	Homepage	**Readability:**	★ ★ ★ ★
Updating:	Monthly	**Reliability:**	★ ★ ★
Navigation:	★ ★ ★ ★	**Speed:**	★ ★ ★

US

This memoir of a gardener's year in Oregon, provides wise words on life and gardening from a garden philosopher. It is divided into 12 beautifully-written monthly journal entries of a satisfyingly meaty length which make absorbing reading. Although the text is clear and nicely presented, there's very little in the way of visual diversion and there is a lot to read, so it's probably best to download the pages and read them offline.

www.esatclear.ie/~emal/			
A Small Irish Garden			
Overall rating: ★ ★ ★			
Classification:	Homepage	**Readability:**	★ ★ ★
Updating:	Regularly	**Reliability:**	★ ★ ★
Navigation:	★ ★	**Speed:**	★ ★ ★

IRE

A lovely site by a real garden enthusiast, with features on her garden, a diary, and a record of garden projects. Scroll down the homepage past the introduction to reveal the contents list and access the main sections of the site. A drop down menu is situated at the bottom of each page, although it's easier to use the browser's back button to move around.

SPECIAL FEATURES

A multi-award-winning, detailed personal site, with plant features (roses, clematis, hardy geraniums) as well as regular diary entries and extensive articles on features and projects, illustrated by the author's own photos. There's a guestbook, and the site is a member of many webrings.

www.alfresco.demon.co.uk
An English Country Garden

Overall rating: ★ ★ ★

Classification:	Homepage	**Readability:**	★ ★ ★ ★ ★
Updating:	Monthly	**Reliability:**	★ ★ ★ ★
Navigation:	★ ★ ★ ★ ★	**Speed:**	★ ★ ★ ★

UK

Details of a cottage garden in Netherbury, Dorset, which is easy to navigate and has an up-to-date monthly diary and plenty of garden advice. The well-designed homepage leads to sections which contain clear and simple information, which is of most use to beginners. The descriptive garden tour and diary, however, hold plenty of interest for anyone who enjoys observing the gardening progress of others.

www.simplegiftsfarm.com
Doug Green's Gardening Tips

Overall rating: ★ ★ ★

Classification:	Homepage	**Readability:**	★ ★ ★ ★
Updating:	Monthly	**Reliability:**	★ ★ ★ ★
Navigation:	★ ★ ★ ★	**Speed:**	★ ★ ★ ★

US

Doug Green is a published garden writer and radio presenter with around twenty years experience of running his own nursery business and his site offers advice on most gardening subjects. You can also subscribe to a free weekly email newsletter, which contains a feature and answers gardening queries. Graphics are deliberately kept to a minimum and tend to be low quality, so that you can download at maximum speed.

www.rain.org/~philfear/garden.html			
Gardening as an Anarchist Plot			
Overall rating: ★ ★ ★			
Classification:	Homepage	**Readability:**	★ ★ ★
Updating:	Occasionally	**Reliability:**	★ ★ ★
Navigation:	★ ★ ★	**Speed:**	★ ★ ★

(US)

Gardening is a pastime for all sorts of interesting people, as this quirky site demonstrates. Don't be put off by the title; although the site has a strong vegetarian and organic emphasis, there are few politics in evidence. The advice for the serious organic gardener is sound and covers topics such as comparison and container planting, herb growing, solar power and cruelty-free rodent repellents.

SPECIAL FEATURES

1998: The Year of the Urban Terracist Handy hints on how to selectively grow herbs in a confined space with limited sunlight

Sacred Herbs A rather spooky looking section, which discusses the interface between science and magic and describes the medicinal properties of herbs.

A unique site with solid information on organic gardening both in rural and urban environments.

OTHER SITES OF INTEREST

Crabfish
www.crabfish.co.uk/gardendiary.htm
In this, the garden section of a site owned by two Brighton-based artists, they describe the making of their wildlife and sculpture garden.

Melon Man
http://www.melonman.com
Bob Dwyer from Missouri, USA, takes growing large melons very seriously indeed. You can follow his progress and advice here, if you really want to try growing melons under the constraints of the British climate.

Urban Garden
www.urbangarden.com
A small but beautifully-designed site dedicated to getting the most from a city container garden. It is subdivided into monthly entries, and each page contains two or three years' worth of chores, hints and favourite plants grown in the garden.

TV Programmes Online

A growing number of TV gardening programmes have websites, from straightforward online factsheets to highly interactive pages. The genre still has room for improvement, although Channel Four is setting the standard.

www.channel4.com/nextstep/fork_to_fork
Fork to Fork

Overall rating: ★ ★ ★ ★			
Classification:	TV Programme	**Readability:**	★ ★ ★ ★
Updating:	As broadcast	**Reliability:**	★ ★ ★ ★ ★
Navigation:	★ ★ ★ ★	**Speed:**	★ ★ ★ ★

UK

A small but very well-researched site which is full of information and resources, featuring the golden couple of TV organic gardening, Sarah and Monty Don. Reports are of a good length and of special interest to those beginning organic vegetable growing for the first time. Information is taken from the Channel 4 programme and updated when the series is running.

SPECIAL FEATURES

Getting Started, Controlling Pests and Making Compost give good, practical advice on the basics of setting up an organic garden.

Monty's House and Philosophy detail the history and design of his garden and give a short insight into the importance of growing and eating organic fruit and vegetables.

Programmes and Recipes show exactly what was tackled in each programme and give lists of suppliers and resources where appropriate. There are a good number of tempting recipes using fresh produce, which are simple and easy to follow.

www.channel4.com/nextstep/real_gardens
Real Gardens

Overall rating: ★ ★ ★ ★			
Classification:	TV Programme	**Readability:**	★ ★ ★ ★
Updating:	As broadcast	**Reliability:**	★ ★ ★ ★ ★
Navigation:	★ ★ ★ ★	**Speed:**	★ ★ ★ ★ ★

UK £

www.gardenersworld.beeb.com
BBC Gardeners World

Overall rating: ★ ★ ★			
Classification:	TV Programme	**Readability:**	★
Updating:	Daily	**Reliability:**	★ ★ ★ ★
Navigation:	★	**Speed:**	★

UK

A useful resource for programme viewers, and especially helpful for inexperienced gardeners. The information on the site is taken from the TV programme whose team of presenters includes Carol Klein, Anne-Marie Powell and Monty Don. Material is updated each week, but unfortunately only when the series is running. The permanent menu bar makes it simple to move anywhere on site, and you can return home by clicking the **Real Gardens** logo.

SPECIAL FEATURES
Programmes are listed in order of broadcasting, with the earliest at the bottom of the list. There are details of the three gardens featured in each programme, a reminder of what was tackled, list of plants, and guide to further reading, suppliers and websites to visit.

A-Z of Garden Plants features a detailed explanation of the meaning of plant names, and gives specific information on terms such as genus, variety, hybrid, and cultivar. A list of plants used in the programmes reveals detailed information when clicked.

A-Z of Common Pests deals with and describes pests in much the same way.

There are also short biographies of the **Presenters**, a guide to **Further Reading** and **Online Resources**.

Charlie Dimmock, Anne Swithinbank, Bob Flowerdew and several other members of Radio 4's Gardener's Question Time bring a wealth of experience to the team of writers who contribute here. The site is mainly of interest to viewers of Gardeners World and other BBC gardening programmes and information is aimed generally at the novice gardener.

Information is excellent and kept up-to-date, daily on some parts of the site. Apart from the main menu, the homepage carries a daily message from the editor, weather information, details of BBC garden programmes and navigation tips. There's also an invitation to join the Gardeners World WebClub, whose members receive a weekly email alerting them to changes on the website and horticultural musings from one of the BBC celebrity gardeners.

This is not a site that reveals itself easily, even to the experienced surfer. It can be slow to download and there are lots of visual distractions such as the over-large menu and header bars, in addition to numerous links. Advertising for BBC products can also be irritating. There are perhaps more features than can be reasonably made use of and it would be improved by the inclusion of a good searchable archive. Nevertheless, it provides, high-quality editorial and a completely new site is planned for a spring launch, which may address some of the existing problems.

Your browser needs to be enabled for Javascript and frames to access the competition, and you'll need RealPlayer (downloadable) to listen to interviews.

SPECIAL FEATURES

The main menu has links to changing features under several different headings:

Garden News presents general items of interest to gardeners and is updated daily.

Action Tips gives general advice on what garden tasks to be getting on with this month. You can browse through previous tips.

Events Diary A comprehensive list of garden-related events for the month. Clicking on the one-line description gives more details and links to relevant sites. There is also a link to the National Gardens Scheme site (see p.120) where you can make a search for gardens open in your area.

Projects gives a number of ideas for landscaping your garden, and you can browse previous articles.

Back to Basics is a series of jargon-free articles on aspects of gardening, such as pest-control, aimed at the inexperienced gardener.

Question Time presents the opportunity to have your tough gardening questions answered by one of the BBC gardening celebrities. A pull-down menu allows you to browse previous questions and their detailed responses.

Garden Wildlife provides a small number of short articles, changed on a monthly basis, aimed at helping you to encourage and identify wildlife in your garden.

SURFING TIPS

The best tip is to use the New to the Web? button on the home page, which takes you to the site's overview.

This site provides top quality editorial and good advice from respected gardeners, although the presentation needs work.

www.beechgrove.co.uk
The Beechgrove Garden

Overall rating: ★ ★ ★

Classification:	TV Programme	**Readability:**	★
Updating:	As Broadcast	**Reliability:**	★ ★ ★ ★
Navigation:	★ ★ ★	**Speed:**	★

UK

This site maintains an archive that contains four years worth of factsheets from the television programme, which is broadcast from gardens in Aberdeen. The factsheets cover each programme fully, which is useful if you missed one or need more information. You need to know what you are looking for though, as there's no facility to search the archives. A no information about the TV programme is provided, this site may be of more interest to viewers of BBC Scotland.

The site is simple to use and most instructions are self-explanatory. Use the foot-of-page navigation bar and click on **Index** to return to the home page.

www.meridian.tv.co.uk/grassroots
Grassroots

Overall rating: ★ ★ ★

Classification:	TV Programme	**Readability:**	★ ★ ★
Updating:	As Broadcast	**Reliability:**	★ ★ ★ ★ ★
Navigation:	★ ★ ★ ★	**Speed:**	★ ★ ★ ★

UK

Homepage of the ITV programme shown in Southeast England, providing sound advice and reliable information on low maintenance gardening. The contents are updated as each programme goes out when the series is running.

SPECIAL FEATURES

This week's programme gives all the information you might need about the programme.

Questions and Answers lists queries from the programmes with their answers.

Factsheets are archived by date and give an extensive report on the programme contents with relevant contact details and lots of background information.

Chapter 4

Spending Money

Marketplaces

Online Garden Centres are becoming increasingly popular as the web's commercial potential begins to be recognised by garden companies and nurseries. Products are grouped together in one shopping centre, or there are links to commercial sites. The sites listed here are among the first few well-designed examples with straightforward ordering, although it's certain that many more will follow suit.

www.birstall.co.uk
Birstall Garden Centre

Overall rating: ★★★★			
Classification:	Ecommerce	Readability:	★★★
Updating:	Daily	Reliability:	★★★★
Navigation:	★★	Speed:	★★★

UK

This site offers secure online ordering on a wide range of garden-related merchandise, all available under one 'roof'. The range of merchandise available is updated daily and there is also a monthly gardening article. You have to concentrate when looking around this site, due to the overly complex navigation system.

SPECIAL FEATURES

This comprehensive and well-planned site includes just about everything you would find in a Garden Centre: Furniture, Barbeques, Sheds, Ponds and Aquariums, Pots, Crafts, and a Nursery and Florist. Products are either supplied and sold online or there are links to other recommended suppliers. You can search for the item you require, and a colour-coded system tells you instantly whether it is available on this site or as a link. You may want to give the video of the inside of the Garden Centre a miss, unless you are really interested, of course.

www.ishop.co.uk
Ishop

Overall rating: ★ ★ ★ ★			
Classification: Ecommerce		**Readability:**	★ ★ ★ ★
Updating: Unclear		**Reliability:**	★ ★ ★
Navigation: ★ ★ ★ ★ ★		**Speed:**	★ ★ ★ ★

UK 🔒

www.oxalis.co.uk
British Gardening Online

Overall rating: ★ ★ ★			
Classification: Ecommerce		**Readability:**	★ ★ ★
Updating: Regularly		**Reliability:**	★ ★ ★
Navigation: ★ ★ ★ ★		**Speed:**	★ ★ ★ ★

UK 🔒

This site provides access to a number of suppliers, all of which provide secure online ordering. Just follow the **Garden Shop** link to browse the suppliers available. Each page is different but generally of a high quality. Links back to ishop on each page make navigation easy.

SPECIAL FEATURES

The site is a portal giving links to **The Garden Supply Company, Teast Trading** (pots and planters), and **Plantpak** (potting trays and containers). All ordering is via ishop and uses their secure system.

A well-organised marketplace site grouping together a number of suppliers under one roof, and hosting the webpages of several UK gardens and nurseries. A good first stop for buying online or finding gardens and nurseries in the UK. The menu on the left gives a comprehensive list of what's available, and there are also direct links in the main text. Click on the BGOL symbol anywhere in the site to return to the home page.

SPECIAL FEATURES

A good selection of plants, seeds and products from a large number of different companies are all available to order from the. You can also use the **Buy, Sell, Swap** facility to place free classified ads or respond to one already posted.

The Garden Finder is a useful search facility, and gives detailed information on a number of UK gardens, many with links to websites.

There's also a plant selector, discussion board, articles and a what's on facility.

www.capitalgardens.co.uk
Capital Gardens

Overall rating: ★ ★ ★			
Classification: Ecommerce		**Readability:**	★ ★ ★ ★
Updating: Unclear		**Reliability:**	★ ★ ★
Navigation: ★ ★ ★ ★		**Speed:**	★ ★

UK 🔒

This London-based mail-order site offers free delivery in the London area, though some options such as Living Plant Sales were not up and running at the time of reviewing. Click on one of the links on the homepage to find the product you require. Though the homepage looks busy, with many of the links duplicated, it's fairly simple to find the page you want. Button bars return you home.

SPECIAL FEATURES
Too many sections to list, but this site carries the range of goods you would expect to find in a garden centre, with the exception of some houseplants, perennials and shrubs. In addition the Troubleshooter page offers illustrated advice on pests and diseases amd other garden projects such as creating a pond.

Plant Nurseries

Not surprisingly, small and specialist mail-order nurseries have been quick to recognise the benefits of online trading. As a result, most of these sites look good and function efficiently, and many offer exceptionally good value for money or extremely interesting or rare plants.

These sites have been listed alphabetically for ease of use.

www.bluebellnursery.com
Bluebell Nursery and Arboretum

Overall rating: ★ ★ ★ ★			
Classification:	Nursery	**Readability:**	★ ★ ★ ★
Updating:	Seasonally	**Reliability:**	★ ★ ★ ★
Navigation:	★ ★ ★ ★ ★	**Speed:**	★ ★ ★ ★

UK

Specialising in rare and unusual plants of all types, this is a very tempting site with a lot to offer the serious gardener with an eye for the unusual. The site is friendly and helpful and the homepage announces that 'We are enthusiastic about most plants'. There is masses of information to be found and the site is supremely clear: use the shopping trolley facility to compile your order which you can pay for by fax, phone or post.

SPECIAL FEATURES

The impressive list of plants offers clear descriptions and some plant history, even folklore when appropriate. Some plants are illustrated with photos. The only drawback is the lack of secure online ordering, but as they are a specialist nursery, some plants are not immediately available, requiring contact with the customer to finalise the order, when payment details can be taken. Otherwise you can send your details by phone or fax.

A tempting site which will appeal to the serious gardener with an eye for the unusual.

www.bodnant.co.uk
Bodnant Garden Nursery

Overall rating: ★ ★			
Classification: Nursery		**Readability:**	★ ★ ★
Updating:	Monthly	**Reliability:**	★ ★ ★
Navigation:	★ ★ ★ ★	**Speed:**	★ ★

UK

Bodnant specialise in shrubs, trees and specialist seeds and stock an extensive collection of Azaleas, Rhododendrons and Camellias. Plant availability is updated monthly and each month a plant is featured in detail, with details of the history, characteristics and suitable growing conditions.

It is possible to order online, though it's not secure and card details can be phoned or faxed.

Navigation is straightforward although it's not a particularly easy site to read with a lot of large, bold type and no illustrations, and some pages can be slow to download.

http://herbs.get-the-web.com
Breckland Herbs

Overall rating: ★ ★ ★ ★			
Classification: Nursery		**Readability:**	★ ★ ★ ★ ★
Updating:	Seasonally	**Reliability:**	★ ★ ★ ★
Navigation:	★ ★ ★ ★	**Speed:**	★ ★ ★ ★

UK

Breckland Herbs is a 20-year-old business offering a huge range of herbs at good prices. The site is maintained regularly and the catalogue is updated seasonally, with just the right amount of information presented in an excellent layout. The only imperfection on this site is the lack of a shopping trolley facility, but it is still possible to order online.

SPECIAL FEATURES

Herb Plugs and Fresh cut herbs can be bought by mail order, both at a very good price which includes post and packing. The range on offer is comprehensive and a few special varieties are offered as well.

A great site which does its job well.

www.eclipse.co.uk/burncoose

Burncoose Nurseries

Overall rating: ★ ★ ★ ★ ★

Classification:	Nursery	**Readability:**	★ ★ ★ ★ ★
Updating:	Regularly	**Reliability:**	★ ★ ★ ★
Navigation:	★ ★ ★ ★ ★	**Speed:**	★ ★ ★ ★

UK

Plants take centre stage at this exemplary site, which is provided by a Chelsea Gold-medal winning company specialising in rare and unusual varieties. To find the plant you want , select Plant Catalogue and indicate the initial letter of the plant you're looking for, and a dropdown menu lists the plants available. Click Show Varieties to view. Ordering is a cinch.

A well designed site, packed with must-haves for the serious plantaholic.

www.farmyardnurseries.co.uk

Farmyard Nurseries

Overall rating: ★ ★ ★

Classification:	Nursery	**Readability:**	★ ★ ★ ★
Updating:	Occasionally	**Reliability:**	★ ★ ★
Navigation:	★ ★ ★ ★	**Speed:**	★ ★ ★

UK

The owners are infectiously enthusiastic about this small but select range of unusual plants, which focuses on hellebores and herbaceous perennials. The site is small and easily navigable with text hyperlinks that are obvious and quick to follow. It's also good to see a site where trouble has been taken to include photographic reference of each plant on offer. However, the information is for reference purposes only, as you can't order online.

SPECIAL FEATURES

Follow the links in the homepage text to lists of **Hellebores, Unusual Herbaceous Plants, Tricyrtis, Schizostylis,** and **Other Plants.**

Take a look at the **Special Announcements** page for interesting news from the owners about varieties bred or discovered at the nursery.

Should you wish to visit, you'll find a map and directions to the nursery which is based in Llandysymul, Carmathenshire.

www.shrubsdirect.com
Grasslands Nurseries

Overall rating: ★ ★ ★

Classification:	Nursery	**Readability:**	★ ★ ★
Updating:	Seasonally	**Reliability:**	★ ★ ★
Navigation:	★ ★ ★	**Speed:**	★ ★ ★

UK

Over 900 varieties of established plants, in one and a half, two and three litre pots, are available from this nursery at wholesale prices.

It's easy to view the site using the permanent toolbar which rests at the foot of the page. The main text sits above this and is viewed by its own scroll bar. Ordering plants means opening another window and entering details manually, but a shopping trolley system is being developed which will address this difficulty. Readability is a little compromised by the location of the toolbar, although the catalogue is clear, and images are slow, but you can download a text-only version of the catalogue.

SPECIAL FEATURES

A good range of high quality plants, in particular shrubs, are offered for mail order at excellent prices. It may be worthwhile ordering by telephone to avoid the awkward ordering system

www.gardenplants.co.uk
Manor Nursery

Overall rating: ★ ★ ★ ★

Classification:	Nursery	**Readability:**	★ ★ ★
Updating:	Seasonally	**Reliability:**	★ ★ ★ ★
Navigation:	★ ★ ★	**Speed:**	★ ★ ★

UK

The Lyall family have been in business for over 30 years and their love of plants comes across clearly on this well-maintained site. A range of herbaceous perennials is listed in the catalogue, which is updated each season. The list is extensive, though the catalogue can be tricky to read, because of the background patterns on the screen. It can also be slow to download, but this can be averted by selecting the older version without the shopping trolley facility. The easiest way to look around the site is to use the browser's back button.

SPECIAL FEATURES

Catalogue page Alphabetical listing of an interesting range of good-sized plants in half to three litre pots. The minimum order is 10 plants but only £5 standard delivery charge.

Photo Album A useful illustrated list of plants suitable for garden interest each month.

News features a photo-diary on the nursery and gardens since 1997. The nursery has been featured on BBC TV and favourably reviewed in the national press.

Chat Page can be accessed through the 'Contact Us' link, and offers a fairly well-used facility for posting messages of a plant-related nature.

www.monksilver.com
Monksilver Nurseries

Overall rating: ★ ★ ★ ★ ★

Classification:	Nursery	Readability:	★ ★ ★ ★
Updating:	Seasonally	Reliability:	★ ★ ★ ★ ★
Navigation:	★ ★ ★ ★ ★	Speed:	★ ★ ★ ★ ★

UK

www.naturescape.co.uk
Naturescape

Overall rating: ★ ★ ★

Classification:	Nursery	Readability:	★ ★ ★
Updating:	Annually	Reliability:	★ ★ ★ ★ ★
Navigation:	★ ★ ★ ★	Speed:	★ ★ ★

UK

Serious plant enthusiasts will find an excellent catalogue of rare and unusual plants, including variegated and wild collected plants, at this tempting site. A very clear permanent header and menu bar makes the site easy to deal with and the site is updated as each new catalogue is published. It is possible to order online, but you have to pay by cheque in the post.

SPECIAL FEATURES

The main catalogue is available to search, browse or download in full. You can also send for the printed catalogue. Each plant is listed alphabetically and described in detail, and a simple click leads you to the shopping trolley system. The catalogue also lists some very rare plants: these are auctioned, and bids are invited.

There's a useful guide to the care and different uses of ferns and grasses, and you can join the mailing list to be kept informed about updates to the website.

A delicious site with many rare gems.

This family-run company brings 25 years of experience to their website, which specialises in wildflower and other native UK plants and seeds. Merchandise is only available by mail order, as there is no online ordering yet. The homepage lists options clearly, and a New Visitor page gives help with navigation.

SPECIAL FEATURES

Wildlife Habitats gives advice and suggestions for introducing native plants into the garden in various different ways, such as marshy areas, wildlife hedgerows and informal lawns.

Product Range lists the large collection of plants and seeds available, including bulbs and corms, climbers, wild roses, and hedge and pond plants.

Although ordering online is not possible, the company offer friendly advice on placing your order by phone, fax or post.

www.orchard-nurseries.co.uk

Orchard Nurseries

Overall rating: ★ ★ ★			
Classification: Nursery		**Readability:**	★ ★ ★ ★
Updating: Bi-annually		**Reliability:**	★ ★ ★ ★
Navigation: ★ ★ ★ ★		**Speed:**	★ ★ ★

UK

Orchard Nurseries claim to be the most established and perhaps largest commercial growers of snowdrops and spring bulbs. Their small site, specialises in mail order supply of snowdrops, aconites and corms such as fritillarias and erythroniums. Autumn and spring catalogues are produced and the site is updated along with these.

Ordering is by post, phone or fax, though Adobe Acrobat Reader is required to download the printable order form. It's worth noting that downloading can be very slow in the afternoons, so it's better to visit in the morning.

SPECIAL FEATURES

The main list of plants is to be found by clicking on **Spring** or **Autumn**, depending on which season's collection is currently being sent out. A more comprehensive list can be found by ordering the full paper catalogue. The **Information Page** explains the importance of sending and planting bulbs 'in the green'.

www.paradisecentre.com

Paradise Centre

Overall rating: ★ ★ ★			
Classification: Nursery		**Readability:**	★ ★ ★ ★
Updating: Unclear		**Reliability:**	★ ★ ★
Navigation: ★ ★ ★ ★		**Speed:**	★ ★ ★

UK

The Paradise Centre is a supplier of rare and unusual plants, specialising in bulbous and shade varieties. The site provides an excellent list of plants, each with a full, clear description, although other areas of the site, such as News, were disappointing.

As yet, you can't order online, though the News page promises that this is imminent, but the order forms for fax, phone and postal ordering are easy to use.

SPECIAL FEATURES

Search the catalogue for a specific variety or browse the listings under **Spring/Autumn** bulbs, or **Plants**, listed alphabetically. Clicking on a plant name takes you to a detailed list of varieties, some of which are illustrated.

www.rareplants.co.uk
Paul Christian Rare Plants

Overall rating: ★ ★ ★ ★ ★			
Classification: Nursery		**Readability:**	★ ★ ★ ★
Updating: Regularly		**Reliability:**	★ ★ ★ ★
Navigation: ★ ★ ★ ★		**Speed:**	★ ★ ★ ★

UK

This is a well-maintained and engrossing site provided by a specialist nursery. They offer an excellent collection of rare bulbs, hardy plants and greenhouse species, and have been in business for nearly 30 years. The site is updated to co-incide with the availability of plant lists, as the seasons change. Trouble has been taken to ensure the site is easy to read, with even the backgrounds colour-coded according what's available. Mostly, links are good but you will sometimes need to use your Back button and you may experience some delay downloading the Photo Gallery.

SPECIAL FEATURES

Reception contains hints for getting the most out of the site, with information on what's current, recent changes and obtaining catalogues.

How to Order gives clear details on ordering online or by post, fax, or phone.

Summer and Winter Lists catalogue the immense number of bulbs available at different times of the year, with comprehensive details on each one.

Greenhouse Bulbs lists this extremely interesting and probably unrivalled range.

Photo Gallery is a really excellent resource of carefully catalogued, high-definition images.

www.classicroses.co.uk
Peter Beales Classic Roses

Overall rating: ★ ★ ★			
Classification: Nursery		**Readability:**	★ ★ ★ ★
Updating: Annually		**Reliability:**	★ ★ ★ ★ ★
Navigation: ★ ★ ★ ★		**Speed:**	★ ★ ★ ★ ★

UK

Peter Beales is a well-respected rose-grower with several books to his name. His nursery is a specialist supplier of old-fashioned, rare and historical roses, which you can order online to be delivered bare-root in winter months. The site is updated annually, with each new catalogue and also as new varieties become available. The sheer number of roses in the catalogue makes for a long list, which is generally easy to read, but more information about individual roses would be welcome when choosing.

SPECIAL FEATURES

Full List of Roses is subdivided into type categories; Alba, Damask, Hybrid Perpetuals, etc. There are no notes on the individual roses, although a brief introduction to each type is given. There is a free advice line for UK callers offering help with choosing varieties.

Special Purposes Chart is a useful resource which gives suggestions for awkward situations based on colour preference. Again, though, there is no further information about the roses, although it is possible to order a catalogue online.

Cultivation gives hints on preparing the ground, planting and pruning.There is also a bespoke design service, details about the Norfolk nursery and some suggestions of rose gardens to visit in the UK.

www.users.globalnet.co.uk/~pottino1
Potterton and Martin

Overall rating: ★ ★ ★

Classification:	Nursery	**Readability:**	★ ★ ★	
Updating:	Bi-annually	**Reliability:**	★ ★ ★	
Navigation:	★ ★ ★ ★	**Speed:**	★ ★ ★ ★	

UK

www.hyperstore.co.uk/rose
Rose Cottage Nursery

Overall rating: ★ ★ ★

Classification:	Nursery	**Readability:**	★ ★ ★	
Updating:	n/a	**Reliability:**	★ ★ ★	
Navigation:	★ ★	**Speed:**	★ ★ ★ ★	

UK £ R ℹ

This friendly, helpful site includes information on the nursery and visiting details as well as a comprehensive catalogue of their alpines, dwarf bulbs, dormant bulbs and seeds. There's no online ordering, but you can phone, fax or post your order. The information in the main index can be found in a series of text boxes: scroll down for ordering information and postage charges.

This nursery site offers a vast selection of drought-tolerant plants. You can locate your required plant with the useful search facility, but browsing the catalogue is irksome: plants are listed alphabetically in one enormous list and working steadily from A to Z is the only way to get around. Returning home can also be difficult at times. The ordering process is complex and although you can place your order online, you must post your payment. However, there is an excellent selection of plants suitable for dry areas and this alone makes the site worthy of close attention.

SPECIAL FEATURES

You can search for a named plant or for suggested varieties suitable for particular conditions or requirements, or browse through the catalogue. The catalogue lists plants alphabetically by genus and variety, gives the common name, a short description and summary of its type and hardiness.

To order from the catalogue, submit your preferred quantity, and click **Add Purchase**. Plants are despatched in the growing season.

Though cumbersome, this site is worth a look for the selection of arid-environment plants.

www.romantic-garden.demon.co.uk

The Romantic Garden Nursery

Overall rating: ★ ★ ★			
Classification: Nursery		**Readability:**	★ ★ ★
Updating: Unclear		**Reliability:**	★ ★ ★
Navigation: ★ ★ ★ ★		**Speed:**	★ ★ ★

UK

This nursery offers a large and unusual range of plants, and specialise in the supply of topiary and ornamental standards. The site is easy to move around, until you try and negotiate the catalogue, which is one very long page without a search facility and so is time consuming.

To return home at any time, click on the logo in the top corner.

SPECIAL FEATURES

Apart from an interesting short history of topiary since Roman times, the main feature of the site is the enormous range of plants available for mail order. Listed alphabetically, they range from common box to more unusual and dramatic shrubs and climbers, and are available in a variety of forms such as standards, half-standards and multi-stemmed shrubs. You can order by post, fax, phone or email but since there's no order form, it's probably easier by phone or email.

Seeds

Buying seeds by mail order is excellent value and the web makes it easy to browse information and see what's in stock. It doesn't have quite the same thrill as curling up with a pile of catalogues on a winter's evening, but it's getting there - and it's quick.

www.seeds.albatross.co.uk
Breckland Nurseries

Overall rating: ★ ★ ★			
Classification: Nursery		**Readability:**	★ ★ ★
Updating:	Sporadically	**Reliability:**	★ ★ ★
Navigation:	★ ★ ★	**Speed:**	★ ★ ★

UK

A huge range of seeds is available to order at this site. You can order online, though it's not secure. Alternatively you can print out an order form and order by post or fax. To get to the seed list scroll down past the text on the page entitled **Range of Seeds**. In general, the site is well designed though some pages can be slow to download and those which have been scanned in tend to be a little unclear.

SPECIAL FEATURES
The extensive list of seeds includes cottage garden plants, herbs, vegetables, wildflowers, and organic seed potatoes. There's also an efficient search function and order details. On the homepage there is a link to the nursery website which specialises in wildflower meadows and camomile lawns.

www.chilternseeds.co.uk
Chiltern Seeds

Overall rating: ★ ★ ★ ★

Classification:	Nursery	Readability:	★ ★ ★ ★
Updating:	Seasonally	Reliability:	★ ★ ★
Navigation:	★ ★ ★	Speed:	★ ★

UK 🔒

A thoughtfully-designed site with a simple and clear process for secure ordering online. The site is clear and well-laid out, and information is updated seasonally, when new catalogues are produced.

SPECIAL FEATURES

An alphabetically-listed **Main Catalogue** and searchable **Database** contains over 4000 seeds, including 20 different types of Basil! Currently, the main catalogue only lists flower seeds. If looking for vegetables you must have an idea of what you want first and use the database. However, this may change with the new catalogue. Overall, the database is the best way to search the site.

www.exhibition-seeds.co.uk
Exhibition Seeds

Overall rating: ★ ★ ★

Classification:	Nursery	Readability:	★ ★
Updating:	n/a	Reliability:	★ ★ ★
Navigation:	★ ★	Speed:	★ ★ ★

UK £ R 🔒

A good selection of seeds available through secure online ordering, but placing an order demands concentration.

SPECIAL FEATURES

From the homepage, go straight to **Seed for Gardeners** then click on **Quick Search Vegetable Seeds**. This takes you to the main vegetable seed list: click on the blue-highlighted names to see further varieties. You can also browse sections on **Herbs, Pumpkins, Heirloom Seeds** and, of course, **Seed for Exhibition Growing**. To order, keep a written note of what you require and type it into the details box on the order page.

www.nickys-nursery.co.uk
Nicky's Nursery

Overall rating: ★ ★ ★ ★			
Classification:	?Nursery	**Readability:**	★ ★ ★
Updating:	Unclear	**Reliability:**	★ ★ ★
Navigation:	★ ★ ★ ★	**Speed:**	★ ★ ★ ★

UK 🔒

This is good as a first port of call if you want to grow container plants from seed. The range of seeds is excellent and good advice and instructions are provided. Ordering online is secure and postage and packing is free. On the home page, click on Contents for the clearest overview of what's available, and use the Back button on the browser to move around, as this is easier than following their tips on navigation. It's a readable site, compromised only by confusing page layouts and some very bright colours, both of text and backgrounds.

SPECIAL FEATURES

Mail Order Seeds takes you to the home page of the seed catalogue. The nursery specialises in flower seeds for container growing, and there are more than 35 pages of information about each variety, with sowing instructions and cultural advice. Within this section, you can also browse a large selection of Wildflower Seeds, and Wildflower Seed Collections. The Herb seed catalogue is extensive and lists a comprehensive range of culinary and medicinal herbs.

Images gives an indication of what you might achieve with some judicious planting.

Gardening Articles gives some excellent advice on planting up containers, such as the best way to create a hanging basket and how many plants to use, and how to create a fuchsia basket.

www.seeds-by-size.co.uk
Seeds by Size

Overall rating: ★ ★ ★			
Classification:	Nursery	**Readability:**	★ ★
Updating:	Unclear	**Reliability:**	★ ★ ★
Navigation:	★ ★ ★	**Speed:**	★ ★

UK

If you are interested in buying any quantity of vegetable, flower, or herb seeds, you may like to take a look at this site. You can order seeds by weight, but not online: you will have to print out an order form. Be prepared to spend some time here though, as the text is tightly packed and there are no illustrations. The site says "...for pretty pictures grow my flower seeds...".

www.thompson-morgan.com

Thompson and Morgan

Overall rating: ★ ★ ★ ★

Classification: Nursery	**Readability:** ★ ★ ★
Updating: Occasionally	**Reliability:** ★ ★ ★ ★
Navigation: ★ ★ ★ ★	**Speed:** ★ ★ ★ ★ ★

UK 🔒

Thompson and Morgan has been trading since the mid-1800's and offers an excellent range of seeds and young plants, of interest to both the new and seasoned grower. The catalogue is updated as new seeds become available but only lists the available stock. Ordering is available online and is secure.

The feature **About this site** gives an overview of how to get the best from your visit and the frame menu on the left changes to show the full contents of each page. Return home by clicking the logo or scrolling down the menu for a text link.

SPECIAL FEATURES

There are two main catalogues of interest:

Seed is grouped into lists of seeds by name, seeds by use/type, vegetables by group, and new seeds for 2000. There are tips on using the catalogue and on ordering. Thompson and Morgan stock seed from all over the world.

Young Plants are only available in the UK and include plants, seedlings, bulbs and corms.

Ordering is fairly straightforward, using a shopping trolley system, and there's a page of instructions on using the system if you get stuck. There's also a short history of the company, and a guide to germination.

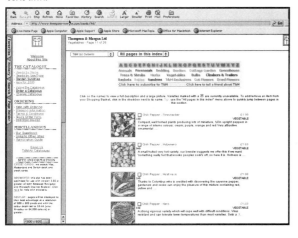

Accessories

From terracotta pots and garden tools to garden furniture and CD-Roms, it's all available to buy online. Again, Britain is still catching up with the US, but secure online ordering is becoming more and more common, and although most firms provide good quality photographs of their products, they are generally happy to answer queries by phone or email first.

www.agriframes.co.uk
Agriframes

Overall rating: ★ ★ ★ ★			
Classification: Shop		**Readability:**	★ ★ ★
Updating: Seasonally		**Reliability:**	★ ★ ★ ★
Navigation: ★ ★ ★ ★		**Speed:**	★ ★ ★

UK

Agriframes is a reliable, well-established company selling good quality garden structures, used by the Royal Horticultural Society in their display gardens at Wisley. Shopping is easy, using a shopping trolley system to order online. Debit and credit cards are taken, and ordering is secure. Information is updated seasonally, and with news items such as sales and promotions. Manoeuvering around the site is straightforward: use the permanent navigation bar at the foot of the page, or the product list at the top.

SPECIAL FEATURES

Reliable ordering of garden arches, bowers, obelisks, pergolas, screens, pondcovers and vouchers. If you want to order by phone, Agriframes ordering staff will call you back at their expense.

www.hurdle.co.uk
English Hurdle

Overall rating: ★ ★ ★ ★			
Classification: Shop		**Readability:**	★ ★ ★ ★
Updating: Unclear		**Reliability:**	★ ★ ★ ★
Navigation:	★ ★ ★ ★	**Speed:**	★ ★ ★

UK

English Hurdle is run by a father and son team, who come from a long line of withy weavers and growers. Their willow products come in both modern and traditional designs, in either seasoned or living wood and gardening enthusiasts can choose from a range including hurdles (fences), trellises, arbors and plant climbers. There's plenty of information about the company and about willow. The only criticism is that some of the product listings are a little lengthy and would benefit from being split into subsections.

SPECIAL FEATURES

About Our Company is a short description of the history and work of English Hurdle.

Range of Hurdles Illustrated product listings accompanied by photos.

Care and Maintenance Instructions for the correct installation of willow products, with tips on how to maximise their lifespan.

An attractive and interesting site, which is simple to move around with the aid of the permanent navigation bar.

www.gardenbooks.freeserve.co.uk
Garden Books by Post

Overall rating: ★ ★ ★			
Classification: Bookseller		**Readability:**	★ ★ ★ ★
Updating: Regularly		**Reliability:**	★ ★ ★
Navigation:	★ ★ ★ ★	**Speed:**	★ ★ ★ ★

UK

Good selection of old and new gardening titles, which are not always at the cheapest possible price but very occasionally beat other booksellers such as Amazon. This site is useful for browsing, but there's no online ordering, just email or phone.

SPECIAL FEATURES

Find what you are looking for under **Offers, New Titles** or **Catalogue**. Some very specialist books are listed but unfortunately you can't make a search.

www.thegardenshop.co.uk
Garden Shop

Overall rating: ★ ★ ★			
Classification: Shop		**Readability:**	★ ★ ★ ★
Updating: Occasionally		**Reliability:**	★ ★ ★
Navigation: ★ ★ ★ ★		**Speed:**	★ ★ ★

UK

A lovely range of good quality garden furniture and other items for outdoor living, but online ordering is a curious procedure and ordering by phone seems the best bet.
Hold your mouse over the page titles on the menu bar for more information.

SPECIAL FEATURES

Products are grouped by type on the main menu: canvas chairs, hammocks, portable furniture and parasols. There is a separate page with ordering details.

www.hortus-ornamenti.co.uk
Hortus Ornamenti

Overall rating: ★ ★ ★ ★			
Classification: Shop		**Readability:**	★ ★ ★ ★
Updating: Unclear		**Reliability:**	★ ★ ★
Navigation: ★ ★ ★		**Speed:**	★ ★ ★ ★

UK

A range of beautiful hand crafted tools, accessories and planters.

SPECIAL FEATURES

Good quality photographs illustrate each product and a shopping trolley facility makes secure ordering simple.

www.pterra.demon.co.uk
Pembridge Terracotta

Overall rating: ★ ★ ★ ★			
Classification:	Shop	**Readability:**	★ ★ ★ ★
Updating:	Occasionally	**Reliability:**	★ ★ ★ ★
Navigation:	★ ★	**Speed:**	★ ★ ★

UK

Pembridge Terracotta produce beautiful hand-thrown pots, made from the local Herefordshire clay, ranging from a few inches in height to a few feet. All pots have a 25-year guarantee against frost damage, providing that they are not left saturated with water, and are porous to enable plant roots to breathe.

Navigation is easy on the homepage but gets more complicated on the order pages. There is a page giving advice on ordering to guide you through the process. Online ordering is secure.

SPECIAL FEATURES

As well as the large range of pots, which are nicely illustrated with watercolour sketches, there are pages showing how the pots are made, ideas for planting and lists of stockists of their pots.

www.plantpress.com
The Plant Press

Overall rating: ★ ★ ★			
Classification:	Shop	**Readability:**	★ ★ ★
Updating:	Unclear	**Reliability:**	★ ★ ★
Navigation:	★ ★ ★	**Speed:**	★ ★ ★

UK

Site where you can purchase the Plantfinder Reference Library CD-Rom, RHS Plantfinder book, and other similar resources. You can order online, and it is secure.

SPECIAL FEATURES

Other features include an online **Dictionary of Common Names,** which will search for keyed-in common or botanical latin names and translate them as required, and the **Horticultural Trades Association Guide to Toxic Plants.**

Chapter 5

Individual Plants and Families

African Violets

www.avsa.org
The African Violet Society of America

Overall rating: ★ ★ ★			
Classification:	Society	**Readability:**	★ ★
Updating:	Regularly	**Reliability:**	★ ★ ★
Navigation:	★ ★ ★	**Speed:**	★ ★ ★

US

A violet-coloured site with growing information, FAQs, indexed articles , a library, linka and plant photos.

Alpines

www.alpinegardensoc.demon.co.uk
Alpine Garden Society

Overall rating: ★ ★ ★			
Classification:	Society	**Readability:**	★ ★
Updating:	Regularly	**Reliability:**	★ ★ ★
Navigation:	★ ★ ★	**Speed:**	★ ★ ★

UK £ R C

A functional site, which is fairly plain and text heavy, but does the job of informing the reader about the society, its activities, shows and local groups. Details are given on how to join.

Annuals

www.discoveringannuals.com
Discovering Annuals

Overall rating: ★ ★ ★ ★ ★			
Classification:	Information	**Readability:**	★ ★ ★ ★
Updating:	Weekly	**Reliability:**	★ ★ ★ ★ ★
Navigation:	★ ★ ★ ★	**Speed:**	★ ★ ★ ★ ★

UK

A lively site promoting the book *Discovering Annuals* by Graham Rice, the award-winning British garden writer who trained at Kew and writes for the London Evening Standard. It is well-designed, with an unambiguous menu, and good photos. The text is clear, authorative and witty and updated every week.

Bamboo

www.bodley.ox.ac.uk/users/djh/ebs
The Bamboo Society

Overall rating: ★ ★ ★			
Classification: Society		Readability:	★ ★ ★
Updating:	Regularly	Reliability:	★ ★ ★ ★
Navigation:	★ ★ ★	Speed:	★ ★ ★

UK

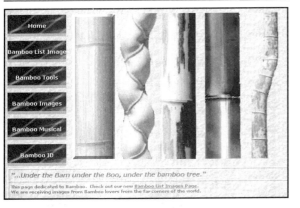

"...Under the Bam under the Boo, under the bamboo tree."

This page dedicated to Bamboo. Check out our new Bamboo List Images Page.
We are receiving images from Bamboo lovers from the far corners of the world.

Up-to-date British contacts and lots of information on growing and making use of bamboo.

Bulbs

www.bulbsociety.com
The International Bulb Society

Overall rating: ★ ★ ★			
Classification: Society		Readability	★ ★ ★
Updating:	Regularly	Reliability:	★ ★ ★ ★
Navigation:	★ ★ ★	Speed:	★ ★ ★

UK

A good starting point for sourcing information about every sort of bulb. The home page appears muddling, but it's worth persevering as the rest of the site functions adequately. To return home, click on the Welcome logo.

SPECIAL FEATURES

There's plenty here for bulb enthusiasts, including news and information in **About the Society** and the chance to Join online using a secure server. Also see **All about Bulbs,** which contains everything from 'what is a bulb?' to sources of rare seed; **Online Discussion**; and **The Gallery,** a useful photographic reference of over two hundred bulbs.

Cacti and Succulents

http://cactus-mall.com/bcss
The British Cactus and Succulent Society

Overall rating: ★ ★ ★			
Classification: Society		**Readability:**	★ ★ ★ ★
Updating: Regularly		**Reliability:**	★ ★ ★ ★
Navigation: ★ ★ ★ ★		**Speed:**	★ ★ ★ ★
UK			

A cheerful little site with good growing information and lots of details on joining the society, which runs special events and conventions, and publishes a quarterly journal.

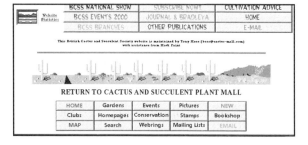

www.graylab.ac.uk/usr/hodgkiss/succule.html
The Succulent Plant Page

Overall rating: ★ ★ ★			
Classification: Homepage		**Readability:**	★ ★ ★
Updating: Monthly		**Reliability:**	★ ★ ★
Navigation: ★ ★ ★		**Speed:**	★ ★ ★
UK			

This is a site dedicated to cactus lovers, which has sections on raising cacti, succulents and other related plants. Amongst the other numerous categories there is information on **Succulent Events** around the world and **Cooking with Cacti**. Cacti photographers can also send in their images for the **Pin Up of the Month** section.

www.cactus-mall.com/mammsoc
The Mammilaria Society

Overall rating: ★ ★ ★			
Classification: Society		**Readability:**	★ ★ ★ ★
Updating: Regularly		**Reliability:**	★ ★ ★ ★
Navigation: ★ ★ ★ ★		**Speed:**	★ ★ ★ ★
UK			

The Mammilaria Society was founded 30 years ago, with the aim of promoting the genus Mammilaria, although the society now covers Corypantha, Escobaria, Thelocactus, Gymnocatus and Nelloctia. The site acts as a brief introduction to the society with plenty of useful contacts, links, and a few articles. Overall there's not a great deal of content, though the site owners hope to expand upon the existing amount. Joining is possible online, and members receive a quarterly journal and access to plant and seed distribution programmes.

Camellia

www.medrz.unisb.de/med_fak/physiol2/camellia/home~.htm
The International Camellia Society

Overall rating: ★ ★ ★			
Classification:	Society	**Readability:**	★ ★
Updating:	Unclear	**Reliability:**	★ ★ ★ ★
Navigation:	★ ★	**Speed:**	★ ★ ★

GER

This is an extensive site, but one which is not easy to get around. Nevertheless, fervent camellia fans might feel able to overlook this.

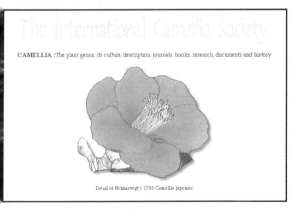

The International Camellia Society

CAMELLIA : The plant genus, its culture, description, journals, books, research, documents and history

Detail of Schneevogt's 1793 Camellia japonica

Canna

www.brockings.freeserve.co.uk
National Collection of Canna

Overall rating: ★ ★ ★ ★ ★			
Classification:	Homepage	**Readability:**	★ ★ ★ ★ ★
Updating:	Occasionally	**Reliability:**	★ ★ ★ ★ ★
Navigation:	★ ★ ★ ★ ★	**Speed:**	★ ★ ★ ★

UK £ R

An exotic-looking site owned by Ian Cooke, holder of the National Collection in Nottinghamshire and author of The Plantfinder's Guide to Tender Perennials. There's plenty of reliable and useful information, displayed in a well-designed and attractive format. Use the button bar at the head and foot of each page, for easy navigation.

SPECIAL FEATURES

History of Cannas is a well-written article on the history of hybridisation and the growth of interest in the plants during the end of the nineteenth and early twentieth century, beautifully illustrated with engravings.

Cultivation offers advice on positioning and protecting cannas, and a guide to planting.

Catalogue of Cannas is a comprehensive, annotated list of species and cultivars in the National Collection.

Canna Gallery displays a large number of named cultivars.

Problems gives brief, clear directions on dealing with the most common pests and diseases.

Mysteries lists varieties suffering from an identity crisis and welcomes opinion on identification.

Carnations

http://website.lineone.net/~dcu/bncs.htm
British National Carnation Society

Overall rating: ★ ★

Classification:	Society	**Readability:**	★ ★ ★
Updating:	Seasonally	**Reliability:**	★ ★ ★
Navigation:	★ ★	**Speed:**	★ ★

UK

A brief online interest which lists contact information for the society.

Clematis

www.yell.co.uk/sites/clematis
Clematis Collection

Overall rating: ★ ★

Classification:	Nursery	**Readability:**	★ ★ ★
Updating:	Seasonally	**Reliability:**	★ ★ ★
Navigation:	★ ★	**Speed:**	★ ★

UK

This specialist clematis nursery provides a small web presence, offering good-sized plants for mail-order despatch or to be sent as a gift. However, the catalogue is not available online, you have to order it by email or post.

http://dspace.dial.pipex.com/town/terrace/pk91/welcome.shtml			
The International Clematis Society			
Overall rating: ★ ★ ★			
Classification:	Society	**Readability:**	★ ★ ★
Updating:	Monthly	**Reliability:**	★ ★ ★ ★
Navigation:	★ ★	**Speed:**	★ ★ ★
UK			

Of interest to serious clematis fanatics. Navigation is via the active text links in each page. To return to the homepage click on the text at the very bottom of the page. There are three useful pages of **FAQ's**, one of which majors on identification from photos. You can browse the questions or email one of your own using the feedback form. Current and previous **Clematis of the Month** can only be accessed from the menu bar which can be found as described above.

www.saska.demon.co.uk/clematis.htm			
T.H. Barker and Son			
Overall rating: ★ ★ ★			
Classification:	Nursery	**Readability:**	★ ★
Updating:	Seasonally	**Reliability:**	★ ★ ★
Navigation:	★ ★ ★	**Speed:**	★ ★ ★
UK			

The site of this specialist Clematis supplier contains a fairly large online catalogue from which you can order by email, including some information on pruning and cultivation .

Cottage Garden

www.alfresco.demon.co.uk/cgs/index.html			
Cottage Garden Society			
Overall rating: ★ ★ ★			
Classification:	Society	**Readability:**	★ ★ ★
Updating:	Regularly	**Reliability:**	★ ★ ★ ★
Navigation:	★ ★ ★	**Speed:**	★ ★ ★
UK			

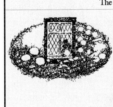

The Cottage Garden Society

The Cottage Garden Society was founded in 1982 by a handful of gardeners in North Wales who hankered after old fashioned flowers grown in the traditional cottage garden style and felt that there must be others who shared their enthusiasm. They were inspired by memories of their parents' and grandparents' gardens, where lilac, honeysuckle and deliciously scented sweet peas gave way to roses and hollyhocks, and where runner beans, lettuces and gooseberry bushes mingled with the marigolds. It seemed to them that there must be many owners of small gardens who shared their aspirations to keep alive these gardening traditions.

At that time such gardens were distinctly unfashionable and were losing the battle for survival to maintenance-free, impersonal, shrub and hard surface schemes. A whole range of plants like old named dianthus or pinks were no longer available commercially. Since then, with the increasing popularity of gardening generally, the growth of interest in plant conservation and the nostalgia for country living, which never lies far below the surface of the British character, membership has risen every year and now stands at around 6000 members world-wide.

Text-only homepage of the Cottage Garden Society, with membership details and information about the seed distribution programme and a list of local groups.

Cyclamen

www.cyclamen.org
The Cyclamen Society

Overall rating: ★ ★ ★ ★

Classification:	Society	**Readability:**	★ ★ ★
Updating:	Frequently	**Reliability:**	★ ★ ★ ★
Navigation:	★ ★ ★ ★	**Speed:**	★ ★ ★ ★

UK

A well-maintained, frequently updated site which has plenty to read. Use the left-hand frame to navigate around the site. There's a useful Site Index link at the bottom of this frame which lists material in greater detail.

SPECIAL FEATURES
There are a good number of pages: The Society, Species and Cultivars, Cultivation, Propagation, Pests and Diseases, Expedition Reports, Bibliography. All are well-written and up-to-date.

Daffodils

www.mc.edu/adswww
American Daffodil Society

Overall rating: ★ ★

Classification:	Society	**Readability:**	★ ★ ★
Updating:	Unclear	**Reliability:**	★ ★ ★
Navigation:	★ ★	**Speed:**	★ ★

US

Useful information on divisions and cultivars, guidelines for growing, naturalisation, and container-growing.

Dahlia

www.swig-online.co.uk/abacus
Abacus Dahlia Nurseries

Overall rating: ★ ★

Classification:	Nursery	**Readability:**	★ ★ ★
Updating:	Seasonally	**Reliability:**	★ ★ ★
Navigation:	★ ★	**Speed:**	★ ★

UK

A small site listing varieties of dahlia for sale as tubers or young plants. Some cultivation tips given. There's no online ordering , so you'll need to fill out an order form and post.

Daylily

www.ofts.com/bill/dl_left.html			
Bill Jarvis's Daylily Site			
Overall rating: ★ ★ ★			
Classification: Homepage		**Readability:**	★ ★
Updating: Unclear		**Reliability:**	★ ★ ★
Navigation: ★ ★		**Speed:**	★ ★ ★
US			

This site is full of information covering such subjects as basic introductions, hybridising, and dealing with crown rot, with good quality photos and clear text too. Unfortunately it also has a bunch of gimmicks. Every link is a new frame and most pages are accompanied by musak. Turn the sound off and be patient if you follow this one up.

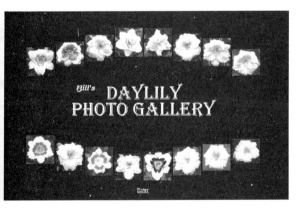

Delphinium

www.delphinium.demon.co.uk			
The Delphinium Society			
Overall rating: ★ ★ ★			
Classification: Society		**Readability:**	★ ★ ★
Updating: Occasionally		**Reliability:**	★ ★ ★ ★
Navigation: ★ ★ ★		**Speed:**	★ ★
UK £ R			

A simple net-presence containing a brief introduction to the society, details on how to join and several other pages of interest to members.

Ferns

www.nhm.ac.uk/hosted_sites/bps/index.htm			
Fern World Wide Web			
Overall rating: ★ ★ ★ ★			
Classification: Society		**Readability:**	★ ★ ★ ★
Updating: Frequently		**Reliability:**	★ ★ ★ ★
Navigation: ★ ★ ★ ★		**Speed:**	★ ★ ★ ★
UK			

This focus for fern enthusiasts is the website of The British Pteridological Society. It's an impressive site, regularly updated with clear text, sensible use of colour and frequent gorgeous photographs. They may take time to download, but are undoubtedly worth the wait. It's an exceptionally well designed site and one which is a delight to read; a real rarity on the net. Use the navigation bars at the top and bottom of each page and clear links to find your way around.

SPECIAL FEATURES

BPS Information on history of the society, membership, publications, local and special interest groups, spore and plant exchange.

Projects Up-to-date information on mapping and distribution projects.

Images A large gallery of high-quality images covering many different varieties and types.

Information 'Where to see ferns' provides an alphabetical list by county of the best places to visit. 'An introduction to ferns' is a highly graphic, beautifully-presented guide.

Grasses

www.grasses.co.uk			
Furzehill Farm Grasses			
Overall rating: ★ ★ ★			
Classification: Homepage		**Readability:**	★ ★ ★
Updating: Monthly		**Reliability:**	★ ★ ★ ★
Navigation: ★ ★		**Speed:**	★ ★ ★
UK			

This non-commercial site is dedicated to ornamental grasses and their cultivation.

It's a fairly experimental site that is sometimes a little unmanageable, and can take a while to load, but nevertheless contains good images and some expert information.

SPECIAL FEATURES

News has a link to a recommended seed exchange.

Grass of the Month is an enthusiastic outline of a selected grass, illustrated with high-quality images.

Propagation of ornamental grasses presents the relevant information in the form of a photo-journal, with high-quality digital images.

Caring for ornamental grasses provides answers to some FAQs.

Geraniums

www.users.bigpond.com/SCRIVENS/index.html
Alby's World of Geraniaceae

Overall rating: ★ ★ ★			
Classification:	Homepage	Readability:	★ ★
Updating:	Continually	Reliability:	★ ★ ★
Navigation:	★ ★	Speed:	★ ★

AUS

This labour of love is a personal site cataloging many different types of the Geraniaceae genus. There's so much crammed onto the pages that it can be a struggle to read, particularly with the detailed wallpaper that appears on many of the pages Some parts of the site, for example a hand-drawn botanical dictionary, are still under construction.

SPECIAL FEATURES

There's a lot of information hidden away here: a large picture gallery and lists of different species, news on taxonomy, book reviews, and seed swaps. Unfortunately the site design is a little on the chaotic side, but it merits examination if this genus interests you.

For the latest additions to the site, click on **What's New?**

Though the design is haphazard, there is a lot of information on this site for lovers of geraniaceae.

www.fitzjohn.linkuk.co.uk
British and European Geranium Society

Overall rating: ★ ★ ★ ★			
Classification:	Society	Readability:	★ ★ ★ ★
Updating:	Seasonally	Reliability:	★ ★ ★ ★
Navigation:	★ ★ ★	Speed:	★ ★ ★ ★

UK

Although the homepage is not especially beautiful, you'll find some excellent advice at a site packed with information. It covers everything you might want to know about the geraniaceae family, including lots of information on pelargoniums, which most of the society's members are interested in. There's also good seasonally updated information on nationwide shows and events. It's not easy returning to the homepage but the navigation bar on left is supremely clear and efficient.

SPECIAL FEATURES

Membership details are on the homepage: scroll down to find them. Otherwise, the navigation bar takes you to information on types and varieties of geranium, a guide to their care: including watering, propagation, overwintering, pest and disease control and a selection of links.

Not an especially good-looking site, but one which holds plenty of interest for geranium and pelargonium lovers.

www.geocities.com/RainForest/Canopy/3139
The Geraniaceae Group

Overall rating: ★★★			
Classification:	Information	**Readability:**	★★
Updating:	Regularly	**Reliability:**	★★★
Navigation:	★★★	**Speed:**	★★★

UK

This site was developed by a small group of British enthusiasts keen to exchange information, share rare seed and preserve wild habitats. The site is regularly updated and provides contact information and examples of the newsletter.

Hardy Plants

www.hardy-plant.org.uk
Hardy Plant Society

Overall rating: ★★★★			
Classification:	Society	**Readability:**	★★★★
Updating:	Occasionally	**Reliability:**	★★★★
Navigation:	★★★★★	**Speed:**	★★★★

UK

A small, clear site which gives an excellent introduction to this intelligent, active society for hardy plant lovers. It covers many aspects of the society's activities such as regional meetings, and lists details of their publications.

The site is well designed site with a minimum of fuss: there's a clear menu and return home facility on each page.

SPECIAL FEATURES

It is possible to join by email, fax or phone, and benefits include local, specialist and correspondent groups, a slide library and seed distribution programme.

Would benefit from more plant information and perhaps sample articles from their excellent publications, but otherwise well worth visiting.

Heather

www.users.zetnet.co.uk/heather
The Heather Society

Overall rating: ★ ★ ★ ★ ★

Classification:	Society	**Readability:**	★ ★ ★ ★ ★
Updating:	Monthly	**Reliability:**	★ ★ ★ ★ ★
Navigation:	★ ★ ★ ★ ★	**Speed:**	★ ★ ★ ★

UK

The Heather Society was formed in 1963 and has a thriving world-wide membership. Their site is an exemplary one which informs the novice and interests the enthusiast, as well as giving details of the society. It contains detailed and easy-to-use information on many different aspects of heather, including choosing, propagating and growing the plant. The different sections are well-maintained and updated monthly when indicated, otherwise seasonally or annually. The site is well thought out for ease of use with clear, well-organised text and pages of manageable size. Finding your way around is simple. There is an informative text introduction containing many quick links, or you can use the menu on the left. Clicking on the Heather Society logo will return you to the home page.

Your browser will need to be able to handle Java in order to search the heather guide and use the design planner.

SPECIAL FEATURES

The Heather Society tells you all you need to know about membership and what to expect.

The Handy Guide to Heather lists more than 1000 cultivars, many with photos, and includes a good deal of plant information and suggestions for sourcing the plants.

Heather Gardens details National Collections, gardens to visit and offers hints for growing, propagating, and designing with heather.

Wild Heathers gives extensive, well-researched information. There's also the opportunity to email Questions which the society attempt to answer within 24 hours.

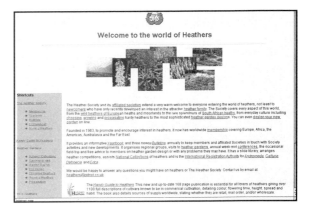

A comprehensive and detailed site, which reveals many of the rare splendours of heather.

Hebes

www.maes-glas.freeserve.co.uk/hebesoc			
The Hebe Society			
Overall rating: ★ ★ ★			
Classification: Society		**Readability:**	★ ★ ★
Updating:	Sporadically	**Reliability:**	★ ★ ★ ★ ★
Navigation:	★ ★ ★ ★	**Speed:**	★ ★ ★ ★
UK			

The society encourages the growing of hebes and also extends its interest to other native plants of New Zealand. Scroll down to the site index for the best overview of what's available on-site.

Updating is fairly sporadic, although at the time of reviewing the site, the list of forthcoming events was up-to-date and information was topical and relevant.

SPECIAL FEATURES

Information is given on how to join the society, which publishes a quarterly journal, holds meetings around the country, and organises a cuttings exchange. There is also a short history of the society.

How to describe your Hebe gives a useful botany lesson with diagrams, on how to identify and correctly name varieties. There are also two pages of photos and some questions and answers on the subject of identification.

Herbs

www.hometown.aol.com/herbring/index.html			
The Herb Ring			
Overall rating: ★ ★ ★			
Classification: Webring		**Readability:**	★ ★ ★
Updating:	Unclear	**Reliability:**	★ ★ ★
Navigation:	★ ★ ★ ★	**Speed:**	★ ★ ★
US			

If you are at all interested in herbs on the web you should take a look at the herb webring, which includes many sites of interest to herb growers.

The lengthy homepage is offputting and is aimed at site owners, rather than users. Scroll to the bottom of the page and click on **Want to Try this Ring** for access to over 200 sites, though not all are related to gardening.

See also The Herb Society, p.99.

www.herbsociety.co.uk
The Herb Society

Overall rating: ★ ★ ★ ★ ★			
Classification:	Society	Readability:	★ ★ ★ ★ ★
Updating:	Monthly	Reliability:	★ ★ ★
Navigation:	★ ★ ★	Speed:	★ ★ ★ ★

UK

This is a near-perfect site, containing plenty of information which would be of interest to the medical herbalist, grower, cook, historian or academic. It is visually stunning, with good quality photographs, and packed full of useful and interesting information about the society which is an educational charity with a worldwide membership. The Information provided is extremely reliable: the society was founded in 1927 and each piece of writing lists the author's credentials at the foot. Content is updated every four to six weeks. The site's only weak point is the lack of a clear menu button bar. Although all the information available is listed at the foot of each page, a briefer list of headings would be clearer.

SPECIAL FEATURES

The Herbmonger gives information and recipes for the use of healing herbs.

Herbal Knowledge updates and informs on plants and their uses.

You can send off for two sets of beautifully photographed herbal greetings cards, and there is a series of well-illustrated articles on plants, cultivation, use and therapy, listed by title, as well as information on membership.

www.botanical.com
Botanical.com - A Modern Herbal

Overall rating: ★ ★ ★			
Classification:	Homepage	Readability:	★ ★ ★
Updating:	Occasionally	Reliability:	★ ★ ★ ★
Navigation:	★ ★ ★ ★	Speed:	★ ★ ★

US

This is the extensive US homepage of 'A Modern Herbal' by Mrs M. Grieve, which was originally published in 1931. The text is clear but the homepage is a little muddled: the easiest way to search for something specific is to do a word search.

SPECIAL FEATURES

With extensive copy listing over 800 herbs and medicinal plants, instructions for cultivation, uses and recipes, **The Modern Herbal** is a fantastic resource and much the best part of the site. However, there are also **Articles**, **Questions and Answers**, **Links** and a **Message Board**, all of which veer strongly towards alternative medicine and 'recreational' herbs.

The **Links** listings are extensive and provide access to many other informative sites for the dedicated herb grower.

www.crabtree-evelyn.com/new/gardtip.html

Crabtree and Evelyn

Overall rating: ★ ★ ★			
Classification: Shop		**Readability:**	★ ★ ★
Updating: Occasionally		**Reliability:**	★ ★ ★ ★
Navigation: ★ ★ ★ ★		**Speed:**	★ ★ ★

US

This is the site of the well-known company selling herbal beauty products. They list some some good tips on design and cultivation ideas of interest to herb-growers. Unfortunately their range of cosmetic products is only available to order in the United States.

SPECIAL FEATURES

Much of the text is taken from 'The Crabtree and Evelyn Fragrant Herbal'. There are sections on **Herb Gardening in Small Spaces,** with tips for container growing and nice ideas for small herb gardens, **Insects and the Garden**: attracting goodies and controlling baddies, and **A Guide to Common Aromatic Herbs and Essential Oils.**

Hostas

www.hosta.org

American Hosta Society

Overall rating: ★ ★ ★			
Classification: Society		**Readability:**	★ ★ ★ ★
Updating: Seasonally		**Reliability:**	★ ★ ★ ★
Navigation: ★ ★ ★ ★ ★		**Speed:**	★ ★ ★

US £ R

General Information and some helpful FAQs.

Irises

www.irises.org			
American Iris Society			
Overall rating: ★ ★ ★			
Classification: Society		**Readability:**	★ ★ ★
Updating: Regularly		**Reliability:**	★ ★ ★ ★
Navigation: ★ ★ ★ ★		**Speed:**	★ ★ ★

US

This site is mostly aimed at the US but the sections on Growing Information and Classifications are relevant and useful to the UK enthusiast, especially keen Iris Growers. (See Hardiness Zones p.11.)

SPECIAL FEATURES

Growing Information provides growing tips suitable for the novice Iris grower to follow, and includes topics such as the Importance of the Rhizome, Preparing the Soil and Thinning and Separating.

Classifications lists the different types of Iris such as Bearded and Beardless varieties, and describes their physical attributes, including height, blooming times and optimum conditions for growing.

Osteospermums

www.gb-nl.freeserve.co.uk/HomePageHome.html			
Osteospermums			
Overall rating: ★ ★ ★			
Classification: Homepage		**Readability:**	★ ★ ★ ★
Updating: Seasonally		**Reliability:**	★ ★ ★ ★
Navigation: ★ ★ ★ ★ ★		**Speed:**	★ ★ ★

UK

A simple introduction to growing and understanding more about osteospermums with just the right amount of photographs to break up the text and illustrate the point. A permanent menu bar lives at the top of the page and makes navigation easy.

SPECIAL FEATURES

Introduction describes the recent rise in popularity and lists new varieties.

Botany is an interesting short article with photos describing leaf and flower form, and a link to a page listing 'all the osteospermums we've ever heard of '.

Propagation gives good advice on taking cuttings and growing osteospermums from seed.

Cape Daisy is a link to Sunshine Plants' website, where osteospermums can be ordered seasonally for mail order delivery.

Roses

www.rosarian.com

The Rosarian

Overall rating: ★ ★ ★ ★ ★			
Classification:	Magazine	**Readability:**	★ ★ ★ ★ ★
Updating:	Regularly	**Reliability:**	★ ★ ★ ★
Navigation:	★ ★ ★ ★	**Speed:**	★ ★ ★

UK

A beautiful online magazine which collates all the GardenWeb resources related to roses in one delicately illustrated compendium. The pages are well laid-out with text, space, and illustration in good proportion to one another. The image-rich pages do take more time to download but the wait is worth it.

A link to the homepage is given on all pages, from where you can find your way around. Joining the mailing list allows notification when new pages or information are added to the site.

SPECIAL FEATURES

Roses FAQs are taken from the forums, and the well written answers are provided by visitors and site staff. There is no index system or archive, though, just scroll down to browse the entries.

Rose Forums There are eight separate forums, covering different topics such as antique roses and rose-growing in Europe.

Gertrude Jekyll on Roses As an ongoing project, whole chapters of Miss Jekyll's classic text, Roses for English Gardens, are being made available to read on screen.

Rose prints by Redouté A small number of on screen reproductions of these exquisite prints can be viewed, and these are also being added to regularly.

Roses in Literature A small, beautifully-illustrated selection of literary quotes about roses, including Alice in Wonderland and Shakespeare's sonnets.

Roses in Art A few examples of roses depicted by notable painters can be clicked and enlarged.

Glossary of terms This regularly updated, searchable database contains more than 3500 botanical and horticultural terms.

Rose Gardens is a smaller, searchable database of gardens around the world where roses may be seen.

An evocative, delicately illustrated compendium of roses

www.roses.about.com

Roses.About.com

Overall rating: ★ ★ ★ ★			
Classification:	Information	Readability:	★ ★ ★ ★
Updating:	Fortnightly	Reliability:	★ ★ ★
Navigation:	★ ★ ★ ★	Speed:	★ ★ ★

US

This is a another branch of the About.com network containing a compendium of links and searchable articles on rose-related matters. It's a useful resource and a good place to start looking for specific information about any aspect of growing or appreciating roses. All the articles are written by Ted Bissland, a writer and former Director of the Canadian Rose Society. Information can be found in the Content section of the top menu bar. This is a permanent fixture and makes navigation easy from anywhere in the site.

SPECIAL FEATURES

Articles displays three years worth of fortnightly articles covering anything rose-related, from the romantic history of old roses to dealing with blackspot.

Netlinks is a resource of garden-related websites and About.com articles, which are listed alphabetically. When these links are followed an About.com toolbar floats above, making it easy to return to the main site.

Search offers the facility to search the site or the whole of About.com.and is perhaps the most efficient way of approaching the information available.

Related has links to other About.com pages which may be of interest.

Share this site allows you to email pages to a friend.

www.timelessroses.com

Timeless Roses

Overall rating: ★ ★ ★ ★			
Classification:	Information	Readability:	★ ★ ★
Updating:	Occasionally	Reliability:	★ ★ ★ ★
Navigation:	★ ★ ★	Speed:	★ ★ ★ ★

US

A useful resource for the keen rose-grower, which contains a good-sized compendium of information about different aspects of rose-growing and detailed listings of individual roses. Overall, the site is nicely designed but the animated banner ads are diverting. Links are not always obvious or reliable and you may need to navigate using your browser.

At the time of writing this review, an additional site, www.gardenwithus.com, was planned, to cover perennials in the same way.

SPECIAL FEATURES

Search for Roses allows you to search the site by individual rose names or by using keywords such as pruning, fragrance or colour.

Glossary has a helpful list of terms covering everything from 'arching shrub' to 'sucker'.

There are a number of articles archived under various headings. **Features** covers general topics such as unusual colours and the history of roses, **Caring For Your Roses** explains how to feed your roses and deal with pests and disease, **Fragrance** attempts to uncover the nature of fragrance and also lists the best choices.

Roses by Class lists all types of roses and Roses for Beginners lists easy-care varieties. Both lists give a full and useful description of each rose, including class, introduction and parentage, flower, size and fragrance, with additional comment on growth, cultivation and any further information of interest.

What's new lists new and recommended varieties.

www.country-lane.com/yr/
Yesterday's Rose

Overall rating: ★ ★ ★ ★			
Classification:	Homepage	**Readability:**	★ ★ ★ ★
Updating:	Occasionally	**Reliability:**	★ ★ ★
Navigation:	★ ★ ★	**Speed:**	★ ★ ★

US

This is a highly visual tribute to old and old-fashioned roses and a beautiful site for rose-lovers, which is useful when choosing varieties. The site is updated as new varieties as new roses are added to the list. Scroll down the homepage to 'View the Roses'. Click on a rose image to view a list of roses from one of 12 groups such as China Tea and Damask, then select a variety and click to see a gorgeous photo and a page of text devoted to its history, appearance and cultivation.

SPECIAL FEATURES

View the Roses is the best bit, but there's also information on **Care and Culture** (including pruning tips with photos) and a link to the US nursery.

A beautiful site for rose lovers, which is especially useful in choosing varieties.

www.classicroses.co.uk
Peter Beales Classic Roses

Overall rating: ★ ★ ★ ★			
Classification:	Nursery	Readability:	★ ★ ★ ★
Updating:	Seasonally	Reliability:	★ ★ ★ ★ ★
Navigation:	★ ★ ★ ★	Speed:	★ ★ ★ ★ ★

UK

www.fryers-roses.co.uk
Fryers Roses

Overall rating: ★ ★			
Classification:	Nursery	Readability:	★ ★
Updating:	Unclear	Reliability:	★ ★ ★ ★
Navigation:	★ ★ ★	Speed:	★ ★

UK

Specialists in old-fashioned, rare and historical roses, this site is fully reviewed in the section on buying plants (see p.73), but many pages within the site have non-commercial interest:

Full List of Roses is subdivided into type categories such as Alba, Damask, Hybrid and Perpetuals. There are no notes on the individual roses, although a brief introduction to each type is given. There is a free advice line for UK callers offering help with choosing varieties.

Special Purposes Chart is a useful resource which suggests roses suitable for difficult environments, based on colour preference. Again, though, there is no further information about the roses, although it is possible to order a catalogue online.

Cultivation gives hints on preparing the ground, planting and pruning.

A reliable, Chelsea Gold Medal-winning firm producing good stock, though online ordering is not an option at the site.

SPECIAL FEATURES
There's a good photographic sample of roses available in the print catalogue which you can order by email. The roses are sub-divided into groups and are mostly modern; Hybrid Teas, Floribundas, Patio Roses and Climbers.

www.inmind.com/people/hughest/roses/redoute.htm

Redouté Roses

Overall rating: ★ ★ ★			
Classification: Homepage		**Readability:**	★ ★ ★ ★
Updating: Occasionally		**Reliability:**	★ ★ ★
Navigation: ★ ★ ★		**Speed:**	★ ★

US

Tom Hughes of Virginia has collated 160 of these exquisite rose drawings by Pierre-Joseph Redouté, a French painter of the late eighteenth century, whose book of prints, Les Roses, captures images of roses from the famous rose garden of Empress Josephine. Click on a named rose to see the image.

www.davidaustinroses.com

David Austin Roses

Overall rating: ★ ★ ★			
Classification: Nursery		**Readability:**	★ ★
Updating: Continually		**Reliability:**	★ ★ ★
Navigation: ★ ★ ★		**Speed:**	★ ★ ★

UK

This site is currently under construction, and although you can order a paper catalogue, it was not possible to order roses at the time of reviewing. The search facility allows you to search for a rose using categories of type, colour and petal formation.

Trees

www.trees.org.uk
The Arboricultural Association

Overall rating: ★ ★ ★ ★			
Classification: Association		**Readability:**	★ ★ ★ ★
Updating: Regularly		**Reliability:**	★ ★ ★ ★
Navigation: ★ ★ ★ ★		**Speed:**	★ ★ ★ ★

UK

This site is useful if you have a particular interest in trees and shrubs, and also perhaps if you have a problem tree, since the association offers help selecting tree surgeons and specialists, and holds a list of approved contractors. There are details of conferences and seminars.

Wildflowers

www.merseyworld.com/landlife
Landlife

Overall rating: ★ ★ ★			
Classification: Charity		**Readability:**	★ ★ ★
Updating: Unclear		**Reliability:**	★ ★ ★
Navigation: ★ ★ ★		**Speed:**	★ ★

UK

You may be interested in knowing about this educational charity which aims to create new habitats for wildlife, particularly in cities.

The site provides information about the organisation and the National Wildflower Centre, due to open in 2000. There is also useful advice on creating your own wildflower environment and where to obtain wildflower seeds and plants. A catalogue of wildflower seed and plants is available and you can email questions.

Click on the coloured text to move around the various sections of the site.

Chapter 6

Online Resources

Garden Visiting

Perhaps one of the ways the web can be of most use to gardeners is in providing information on places to visit. Often, a site will give a whistle-stop visual 'tour' as well as practical details, making it of equal interest to the armchair gardener. These sites are organised into two lists; the first presupposes you know where you want to go, and the second allows you to browse or search a number of databases and discover what's available where and when. All sites are listed alphabetically.

www.barnsdalegardens.co.uk
Barnsdale Gardens

Overall rating: ★ ★ ★			
Classification:	Gardens	**Readability:**	★ ★
Updating:	Regularly	**Reliability:**	★ ★ ★ ★
Navigation:	★ ★	**Speed:**	★ ★ ★ ★

UK £ R

This site makes essential browsing for fans of Geoff Hamilton, the late presenter of BBC's TV's Gardener's World and creator of the Barnsdale Gardens. There are detailed descriptions of each part of the garden he designed and made, although the text layout can be a bit haphazard. Use the links on the menu bar to get around the site.

SPECIAL FEATURES

On the surface this seems a fairly multi-layered site but on closer inspection the **Descriptive Tour** of the gardens at Barnsdale is far and away the biggest and best part. Each section of the gardens, as designed and created by Geoff Hamilton before his death, is listed and described, with an overall map of the gardens for reference. There's a page of biography about Geoff Hamilton, and directions, opening times and all the relevant information needed if you plan to visit. There also happens to be an excellent and well-researched page of links.

www.cpgarden.demon.co.uk
Chelsea Physic Garden

Overall rating: ★ ★ ★			
Classification: Gardens		**Readability:**	★ ★
Updating: Sporadically		**Reliability:**	★ ★ ★ ★
Navigation: ★ ★ ★		**Speed:**	★ ★

UK

This site comes in two versions: Shockwave Flash, a highly interactive multimedia experience, or text only, which is a single long page of straightforward information.
If you require simple, efficient information retrieval, use the text-only version. The Flash version is graphically excellent but can be ambiguous and time-consuming. Navigate around the site by clicking on the yellow dot, and click around on the individual pages to locate images and text.

Shockwave Flash software is necessary if you want to experience the hi-tech version: you can download this from the site.

SPECIAL FEATURES

On either version, the site gives information about the History, Education Programmes and Research undertaken by the garden, which was founded in 1673, and amongst other things, maintains a seed bank of global importance. It also gives details of what can be seen; the garden holds the National Collection of Cistus, and there are trails devoted to endangered peoples and the practice of genetic engineering. There is also information on how and when to visit the garden, which serves refreshments and also has plants for sale.

www.edenproject.com
Eden Project

Overall rating: ★ ★ ★ ★ ★			
Classification: Gardens		**Readability:**	★ ★ ★ ★ ★
Updating: Continually		**Reliability:**	★ ★ ★ ★
Navigation: ★ ★ ★ ★		**Speed:**	★ ★ ★ ★

UK

This is the site of the soon to be completed Eden Project in Cornwall and is well worth a visit if you're at all interested in sustainability and plant history. Information is focused on the role of plants in human culture and human dependence on them. It's a beautifully-designed site, which is continually updated to provide new information on the ongoing project.

Click on the leaf logo to read the welcome message.

SPECIAL FEATURES

A fascinating project with plenty to explore on the site.

Plant Facts Quiz on the role of plants in our lives.

Plants and People How humans and plants interact with one another

The Site Plan of the site and an overview of site development.

Children's Page Facts for kids and a quiz.

www.rbge.org.uk
Edinburgh Royal Botanical Gardens

Overall rating: ★ ★ ★ ★			
Classification: Gardens		**Readability:**	★ ★ ★ ★
Updating: Regularly		**Reliability:**	★ ★ ★ ★ ★
Navigation: ★ ★ ★ ★ ★		**Speed:**	★ ★ ★ ★

UK

A huge, text-only botanical resource which is well designed and efficiently cross-referenced and has clear text and links. News is updated as it happens, and you can arrange to be emailed when the site changes.

SPECIAL FEATURES

The main menu is extensive; if you plan to visit, look up **Visitor Information** and **Events** to find out what's happening. The Search facility allows you to name a plant and find its exact location in the gardens.There's also masses of well-organised information on the collections, research and publications.

www.heligan.com
The Lost Gardens of Heligan

Overall rating: ★ ★ ★ ★			
Classification: Gardens		**Readability:**	★ ★ ★
Updating: Frequently		**Reliability:**	★ ★ ★ ★
Navigation: ★ ★ ★ ★		**Speed:**	★ ★ ★ ★

UK

This is a concise introduction to the gardens at Heligan in Cornwall, which remain as a unique example of a victorian garden. The site design captures the secret Victorian feel of the garden well, and makes use of interesting graphics.

You can click on a series of Victorian icons or text alternativesto find your way around. If you hold your mouse over the icon, the title of the section will appear. Click on the magic lantern icon anywhere it appears to see slides of the gardens. You can also view a webcam image of the garden which is updated every few days.

SPECIAL FEATURES

As well as a number of other features, the site's **Information for Visitors** tells you all you need to know if you are planning a visit, and **Explore** gives a taste of the garden through descriptions, photos, and a seasonal report.

Lost Gardens of Heligan gives a history of the gardens and tells how they came to be lost and rediscovered.

www.hillier.hants.gov.uk
Sir Harold Hillier Gardens and Arboretum

Overall rating: ★ ★ ★ ★ ★			
Classification: Gardens		**Readability:**	★ ★ ★ ★
Updating: Regularly		**Reliability:**	★ ★ ★
Navigation: ★ ★ ★ ★ ★		**Speed:**	★ ★ ★ ★

UK

An excellent introduction to this lovely garden, beautifully hosted by the extremely web-wise Hampshire County Council. The site is illustrated with just the right number of good quality photos, which give you a taste of the garden without compromising the download speed of the site. It requires very little effort to move efficiently around the site, and Hantsweb make it easy to follow up links to their other online resources too.

SPECIAL FEATURES

About the Gardens has an introduction, opening hours, directions, garden plan and history of the gardens.

What's On has a comprehensive programme of guided tours, evening talks, workshops and family events.

Seasonal Attractions devotes a page to showcasing the plants and trees which look their best in each season of the year.

National Collections gives details of the many national collections of trees and large shrubs held by the gardens, which include oak, hazel and privet.

www.rbgkew.org.uk
Kew Royal Botanic Gardens

Overall rating: ★ ★ ★ ★			
Classification: Gardens		**Readability:**	★ ★ ★ ★
Updating: Regularly		**Reliability:**	★ ★ ★ ★ ★
Navigation: ★ ★ ★ ★ ★		**Speed:**	★ ★ ★ ★

UK

An impressive amount of easily obtainable information, which is topical and regularly updated. Written information and searchable databases give detail on both the gardens and the scientific work that goes on there. Information of interest to visitors can be easily found at the top of the homepage. Straightforward text makes this more of a practical site for information retrieval than a visual experience, but it's nevertheless a fast and efficient resource of a high standard.

SPECIAL FEATURES

Visit the Gardens gives essential information if you plan a visit, from the practicalities of location and admission to details of what to see.

Databases allows you to search online for a wide range of information on plant families and particular uses for plants around the world.

Other Sites is a comprehensive alphabetical listing of sites and is a good starting point if you're looking for online resources on botanical issues.

The more scientific pages are listed towards the foot of the home page; **The Collections** has details of both living and preserved plants, **Heritage** gives some of the fascinating history of both the gardens and buildings.

www.knebworthhouse.com
Knebworth House

Overall rating: ★ ★ ★			
Classification: Stately Home		**Readability:**	★ ★ ★
Updating: Unclear		**Reliability:**	★ ★ ★
Navigation: ★ ★ ★		**Speed:**	★ ★ ★
UK			

The gardens section is just one area of this site about the Medieval stately home. There's a map of the gardens, visiting details and a page describing each of the gardens, accompanied by photographs. More information about the actual plants and garden design would be helpful for garden visitors.

Getting to the gardens is self-explanatory: just click on the **Knebworth Gardens** heading on the menu bar.

www.cix.co.uk/~museumgh
Museum of Garden History

Overall rating: ★ ★ ★			
Classification: Museum		**Readability:**	★ ★ ★
Updating: Unclear		**Reliability:**	★ ★ ★
Navigation: ★ ★ ★ ★		**Speed:**	★ ★ ★
UK			

A quirky and interesting site which whets the appetite for a visit to The Museum of Garden History, and is full of fascinating facts about the history of many of the plants grown today.

SPECIAL FEATURES

About the Museum gives details and describes the aims of the Tradescant Trust, set up in 1977. The museum has exhibitions on the history of garden plants, famous gardeners and plant-hunters.

A Virtual Visit shows the main features of the museum including the Tradescant Garden, a replica seventeenth century knot garden where Captain Bligh of The Bounty and the Tradescants are buried. Downloading parts of the tour can take a little time, but it's worth the wait. Use the browser's back button to navigate.

A History of the Museum is a fascinating and lengthy description of the history of the site and it's associations with the Tradescants and Elias Ashmole.

There's also information about becoming a friend of the Trust.

A tempting site, reflecting the character of the Museum of Garden History.

www.merseyworld.com/nessgardens

Ness Botanical Gardens at the University of Liverpool

Overall rating: ★ ★ ★ ★ ★			
Classification: Gardens		**Readability:**	★ ★ ★ ★ ★
Updating: Seasonally		**Reliability:**	★ ★ ★
Navigation: ★ ★ ★ ★		**Speed:**	★ ★ ★ ★

UK

It's rare to find a site like this one that does justice to the gardens it describes. This site is an excellent read, and well chosen text is accompanied by high definition photos, which are relatively quick to download. Information is reviewed seasonally and the programme of events is updated as necessary. You can return home from each page or follow the virtual tour by clicking Next after each section.

SPECIAL FEATURES

Introduction to the Gardens is a well-written, interesting article charting the history of Ness from past to present and its associations with plant hunters of the early twentieth century.

Virtual Tour provides exceptionally detailed descriptions of each main area of the garden, giving its individual history and listing plants of particular seasonal interest.

General Information covers visiting, facilities and admission.

Exhibitions and Events give an up-to-date indication of what's going on, an impressive list including lectures, courses, festivals and weekly summer exhibitions.

Planning a Visit contains some helpful databases.

Databases of Gardens

www.english-heritage.org.uk
English Heritage

Overall rating: ★ ★ ★			
Classification:	Information	**Readability:**	★ ★ ★
Updating:	Unclear	**Reliability:**	★ ★ ★
Navigation:	★ ★ ★	**Speed:**	★ ★ ★

UK

English Heritage manage and maintain some important gardens, such as Fountains Abbey and the royal park and gardens at Osborne House. This site concentrates on the achaeological and historical interests of the organisation and you probably need a fair amount of knowledge on which properties have the best gardens, as such details are not listed separately. To access a list of properties in your area, select your region from the map of England on the home page.

www.cults.dircon.co.uk/ebg
Essential British Gardens

Overall rating: ★ ★ ★			
Classification:	Webring	**Readability:**	★ ★ ★ ★
Updating:	Unclear	**Reliability:**	★ ★ ★ ★
Navigation:	★ ★ ★ ★	**Speed:**	★ ★ ★ ★

UK

This site is 'A digest of some of the finest gardens and arboretums throughout Britain' and though it does not promise to be exhaustive, it nevertheless is quite comprehensive. It's a clear and well laid out site, though its main function is to provide links to other sites which all have their own idiosyncracies. There's lots of hints on how to get around. If you follow a link you'll need to use your browser's Back button to return to Essential British Gardens.

SPECIAL FEATURES

On the homepage, select an area of the country, which will summon up an alphabetical list of gardens for that region. Most have links to follow to websites which will give visiting details.

The **Search** facility is only of limited value as the results are very general.

www.dublingardens.com
Dublin Garden Group

Overall rating: ★ ★ ★ ★ ★

Classification:	Gardens	Readability:	★ ★ ★
Updating:	Occasionally	**Reliability:**	★ ★ ★
Navigation:	★ ★ ★	**Speed:**	★ ★ ★

IRE

A small and select group of personal gardens not all usually open to the public which can be visited in organised groups by contacting the website.

SPECIAL FEATURES

Garden Pages gives details of the individual gardens, which include the well-known Dillon Garden, as well as some smaller suburban gardens.

www.s-h-systems.co.uk/tourism/london /parks.html
London Parks and Gardens

Overall rating: ★ ★ ★

Classification:	Information	Readability:	★ ★ ★
Updating:	Unclear	**Reliability:**	★ ★ ★
Navigation:	★ ★ ★	**Speed:**	★ ★

UK

Lists the main gardens in London which are open to the public, and provides a page of text giving details of what to see, with links to relevant places of interest, opening times when appropriate, and nearest tube stations.

www.nationaltrust.org.uk
National Trust

Overall rating: ★ ★ ★ ★			
Classification:	Information	Readability:	★ ★ ★ ★ ★
Updating:	Seasonally	Reliability:	★ ★ ★ ★
Navigation:	★ ★ ★	Speed:	★ ★ ★ ★ ★

UK

The National Trust cares for over 300 buildings and gardens in England, Wales and Northern Ireland. This beautifully-designed site provides very clear, concise, yet comprehensive information about many individual properties and gardens. Information is revised seasonally to provide the relevant information about visiting details.

SPECIAL FEATURES

Places to Visit Gardens and properties are listed alphabetically or by selecting one of nine areas covering England, Wales and Northern Ireland. You can also search for properties by county, individual name or by theme. When you have found the property or garden you're looking for, click again and extensive details are given about the nature of the property, directions, admission and opening arrangements, and other details. When viewing search results you'll need to use the **back** button on the browser, otherwise click on the relevant section at the top of the page.

There is a useful **Key to Symbols**, and **Essential Information for Visitors** gives general guidelines, including sections on visiting with families, and information for those with disabilities.

A useful search facility covering many parks and gardens

www.nts.org.uk
National Trust for Scotland

Overall rating: ★ ★ ★			
Classification:	Information	Readability:	★ ★ ★ ★
Updating:	Regularly	Reliability:	★ ★ ★
Navigation:	★ ★ ★	Speed:	★ ★ ★ ★ ★

UK

This site provides information on the properties and gardens of the National Trust for Scotland.

Click on **Properties to Visit** and select the area of Scotland you wish to explore. Properties and gardens are then listed alphabetically. Use the Back button on your browser to return to the list. The menu bar is a little unclear on some browsers but otherwise the information is well-presented and visiting details are kept up-to-date.

SPECIAL FEATURES

Properties to Visit leads you to the main visitor information, where details of opening times, what to see and whether there is a shop or refreshments, are given for each property or garden.

Conservation in Action also contains an interesting article on Scotland's Garden Scheme and garden conservation issues.

www.york.ac.uk/depts/arch/landscapes/ukpg/database/index.htm

UK Database of Parks and Gardens

Overall rating: ★ ★ ★			
Classification:	Information	Readability:	★ ★ ★ ★
Updating:	Unclear	Reliability:	★ ★ ★
Navigation:	★ ★ ★ ★	Speed:	★ ★ ★ ★

UK

A resource which lists historic places which are of interest to garden visitors. Listings are brief and the site serves as a starting point for those seeking contact information for a particular location. Information provided on each location is limited, each entry gives details of the relevant local authority, its historic county, grid reference, and list of famous people relevant to the park or garden. Contacts and links for further information are given. More information of relevance to garden visitors would be a welcome addition.

SPECIAL FEATURES

There are four main ways of finding information:

Places Listed Alphabetically is a simple list with a page for each letter.

Places Listed by Authority is useful for searching in a local area.

Places Listed by Type, for example, botanic garden, cemetery, museum, public park.

People Listed Alphabetically is a lengthy list of all those who have some place in garden history.

www.gardenofwales.org.uk/historic/index.htm

Historic Parks and Gardens of Wales

Overall rating: ★ ★ ★			
Classification:	Information	Readability:	★ ★ ★
Updating:	Regularly	Reliability:	★ ★ ★
Navigation:	★ ★ ★	Speed:	★ ★

UK

A helpful site, aimed at assisting those planning garden visits in Wales, with well maintained information, up-to-date visiting details and a map showing the location of all the gardens (although it is small and not easily read.)

SPECIAL FEATURES

Listings for over 65 gardens to visit in North, Mid and South Wales, with a map and visiting details. There is also a link to the website of The National Botanic Garden of Wales (http://www.gardenofwales.org.uk/front.htm) an ambitious and exciting new project due to open in Easter of this year.

www.ngs.org.uk
The National Gardens Scheme

Overall rating: ★ ★ ★ ★ ★

Classification:	Information	**Readability:**	★ ★ ★ ★ ★
Updating:	Fortnightly	**Reliability:**	★ ★ ★ ★ ★
Navigation:	★ ★ ★ ★	**Speed:**	★ ★ ★ ★ ★

UK

The National Gardens Scheme is a charity much beloved of garden visitors, which organises the opening of over 3500 private gardens each year. It publishes 'the definitive guide to private gardens which open to the public', fondly known as the Yellow Book. The home page introduces the scheme, with news bulletins highlighted at the right hand side of the screen. These include information on shows, Yellow Book updates, and news of workshops. The main menu can be found on the left, and is straightforward and clear. The site is smartly laid out using clear, well-defined boxes of text, and with moderate use of attractive photos. You will need a Java-enabled browser to make use of **Gardenfinder**.

SPECIAL FEATURES

Garden Finder allows a search for gardens in three different ways. A map search can be made by hovering your mouse over a map of Britain and homing in on the area of interest. This pulls out a list of counties, which in turn bring up a list of gardens in that area. An advanced search uses keywords, counties, date range and garden name, or a quick search highlights those gardens currently open for visiting. Each garden is clickable, and gives a substantial amount of information, including directions, admission charges, opening dates, and plenty of detail on what can be seen, especially any rarities or special collections. Symbols indicate whether the garden allows dogs or sells plants, denote wheelchair accessibility, and even specify whether

tea includes biscuits or cake. Colour-coded backgrounds indicate whether gardens are open individually or as part of a group, and provide information on opening frequency.

Yellow Book gives a full review of the volume, which lists every sort of garden from alpines to topiary, and includes both tiny cottage plots and grand country seats, and everything in between. There's a direct link to Amazon, who give a good discount.

Beneficiaries gives extensive information on the nine charities who currently benefit from the £1.5 million raised each year by garden visits. There are links to websites when appropriate.

About Us describes the history of the NGS, begun in 1927 and now a national institution.

Events are listed in a calendar format and include everything from the big shows to small specialist plant sales.

Garden Stories is a small archive of personal testimony, recipes, garden journals, and news of interest to gardeners.

Links are grouped into categories, such as nurseries, associations and trusts, and bed and breakfast. The number of sites in each category is given, and new additions are highlighted. A keyword search is also possible.

An exemplary and extremely useful site which functions well and is a pleasure to use.

Link Sites

Most sites contain at least a few links to other pages, but for these sites, it's their raison d'etre. Have a look at some of these if you still can't find what you're after.

www.gardening.about.com
About.com guide to Gardening

Overall rating: ★ ★ ★ ★			
Classification:	Information	**Readability:**	★ ★ ★ ★ ★
Updating:	Fortnightly	**Reliability:**	★ ★ ★ ★
Navigation:	★ ★ ★	**Speed:**	★ ★ ★ ★ ★

UK

The About.com websites describe themselves as "Part of a network of sites led by an expert guide" and they are useful resource and a good place to start if you're looking for specific information. (Also see p.26)

Netlinks is a fairly comprehensive resource of garden-related websites and About.com articles, sorted into groups and listed alphabetically. When these links are followed an About.com toolbar floats above, making it easy to return to the main site.

Search offers the facility to search the site or the whole of About.com.

Related has links to other About.com pages which may be of interest.

www.igarden.co.uk
Igarden

Overall rating: ★ ★ ★			
Classification: Ezine		**Readability:**	★ ★ ★
Updating: Weekly		**Reliability:**	★ ★ ★
Navigation: ★ ★ ★		**Speed:**	★ ★ ★ ★
UK			

This monthly ezine offers a wide range of articles, advice, and a large number of links. The site aims mainly to offer links to other gardening sites or resources and the articles reflect this. Whereas some offer straight, impartial gardening advice, others are written by or on behalf of nurseries and garden-related companies, though all offer advice which is authoritative and updated every week.

The range of subject matter covered is also large and includes garden lighting, planning and design, planting, in addition to gardening shows and events.

Links can be confusing and it's not always clear where you're heading, so it's best to use the search facility. Some of the text is a little too small for comfortable reading.

There is a further rewiew of igarden on p. 31.

SPECIAL FEATURES

Articles are searchable and the best place to do this is probably the **Library**, where a search will turn up links, catalogues and articles by subject.

The Garden Advice Centre Email your own question for a personal reply or click on 'Search for Answers' to scan the answers to previously asked questions. Our test question was answered efficiently and within 12 hours, although it lacked a personal feel.

Other sites contains a lisitng of other linked gardening-related sites. Linked sites tend to be for non- commercial resources, so if you're looking for information only and don't want to but anything, this is probably a good place to start.Each site listing is accompanied by a description of the site, with details such as who owns the site, and what the site is about.

A good resource for finding sites, catalogues and specific subject related matter.

www.oxalis.co.uk
British Gardening Online

Overall rating: ★ ★ ★			
Classification:	Webring	**Readability:**	★ ★ ★
Updating:	Varies	**Reliability:**	★ ★ ★ ★
Navigation:	★ ★ ★ ★	**Speed:**	★ ★

(UK)

British Gardening Online hosts the webpages of several UK gardens and nurseries and this is a good first stop for buying online or finding gardens and nurseries in the UK. The menu on the left gives a comprehensive list of what's available, and there are also direct links in the main text. Click on the BGOL symbol anywhere in the site to return to the home page.

The Garden Finder is a useful search facility, and gives detailed information on a number of UK gardens, many with links to websites.

OTHER SITES OF INTEREST

Garden Websites
www.gardening-sites.swinternet.co.uk
Comprehensive listing of garden-related websites arranged in alphabetical sections.

The Internet Garden
www.internetgarden.co.uk
A number of links here, sorted into category and reviewed, but some were broken and it could do with some updating.

Other Resources

These intensely varied, useful, and interesting sites are simply unclassifiable. Some are browsers' sites, others practical, and all contain information not found elsewhere on the web. They are listed in alphabetical order.

www.gardenweb.com
Garden Web

Overall rating: ★ ★ ★ ★ ★			
Classification: Information		**Readability:**	★ ★ ★ ★
Updating: Regularly		**Reliability:**	★ ★ ★
Navigation: ★ ★ ★ ★		**Speed:**	★ ★ ★ ★

UK

The site's main service is hosting well over 100 forums covering every possible aspect of gardening, and including several specifically for European gardeners, as well as seed and plant exchanges. There are also well-organised links pages and several other features.

There is a quick index on the left hand side, or scrolling down the home page leads you to a more detailed contents list. (Also see , p.138)

SPECIAL FEATURES

Apart form the forums, there is an interactive glossary containing over 3500 horticultural and botanical terms, and a large number of links to other sites organised by subject.

Directory lists links to gardening organisations and plant societies; **Bazaar** concentrates on commercial sites; and **Topics** has links ordered into groups such as roses and wildflowers.

www.scs.leeds.ac.uk/pfaf/index.html
Plants for a Future

Overall rating: ★ ★ ★ ★			
Classification:	Information	**Readability:**	★ ★ ★
Updating:	Regularly	**Reliability:**	★ ★ ★ ★
Navigation:	★ ★	**Speed:**	★ ★ ★ ★

UK

The site is, in its own words 'A resource and information centre for edible and other useful plants' and contains a massive amount of information with an emphasis on ecologically sustainable gardening. The pages share a wealth of experience but time and patience is required to do it justice. The text style requires determined concentration and reading offline may be a better option. It can be difficult to identify where sections begin and end on the home page, which is text-only and rather daunting. It is best to scroll down to the Main Index and use your browser's back button to move to and from here.

SPECIAL FEATURES

Database of useful, edible or medicinal plants is searchable, using different characteristics, for example use, name, genus, habitat. There are over 7000 entries with helpful information including uses and cultivation.

Leaflets are available to read online on a multitude of subjects: **Plants for a Future** itself, its history, community, services, and how to get involved; **Plant Use**, both edible and non-edible, vegan-organics and conservation gardening; **Plants for Particular Habitats**, for example ground cover, the urban garden, and problem places; **Interesting and Particularly Useful Plants**, especially edible perennials.There's also a list of useful links to other sites and suppliers.

http://fff.nhm.ac.uk/fff
The Postcode Plants Database

Overall rating: ★ ★ ★ ★			
Classification:	Information	**Readability:**	★ ★ ★ ★
Updating:	Continually	**Reliability:**	★ ★ ★ ★ ★
Navigation:	★ ★ ★ ★	**Speed:**	★ ★ ★ ★

UK

The aim of this local plant index is to encourage gardeners to plant the native trees, shrubs and flowers which are local to their areas, and it is an extremely useful resource. At the time of reviewing the database was still being compiled, with new information added all the time. There's also plenty of background data explaining how the database functions, how it should be interpreted and its limitations. Navigation is easy, just refer to the permanent button bar which sits at the top of each page.

SPECIAL FEATURES

The site offers a fair amount of introductory material, and explains what a native plant is, why it is important to grow native plants, and how the gardener can help. Checklists of native and endemic species of British plants, insects, and mammals are given, and there is a list of suppliers of seeds and plants of native origin.

To **Search the Database**, first type in the first part of the postcode you are searching for, and you will find tailor-made lists of local plants hospitable to wildlife. A photo and brief details can be viewed.

www.sisley.co.uk			
Sisley Garden Tours			
Overall rating: ★ ★ ★ ★			
Classification: Travel Agent		**Readability:**	★ ★ ★
Updating:	Seasonally	**Reliability:**	★ ★ ★ ★
Navigation:	★ ★ ★ ★	**Speed:**	★ ★ ★ ★
UK			

www.gardendigest.com			
The Spirit of Gardening - Quotes for Gardeners			
Overall rating: ★ ★ ★ ★			
Classification: Information		**Readability:**	★ ★ ★
Updating:	Continually	**Reliability:**	★ ★ ★ ★
Navigation:	★ ★ ★	**Speed:**	★ ★ ★
UK			

An uniquely interesting site especially interesting for armchair gardeners keen to increase their knowledge of well-known gardens. The site is run by a small holiday company which has been offering touring holidays, for the last eight years, around Britain and Northern Europe, to gardens and shows. You can also take a virtual tour of over fifty of these gardens. The website is updated seasonally to reflect the details of tours available. Text is generally well-placed and easy on the eye, but one or two pages don't function very well. Photos take a while to download, but you can choose not to download them, making browsing speedy.

SPECIAL FEATURES

There's plenty of information available about the holidays should you wish to take part, but the most interesting pages for the web gardener are those detailing individual gardens in the Garden Tour. There's a page of text about the gardens and their owners, an optional photograph, and opportunities to buy books by the owners or which include their gardens. Each entry is headed by a well-chosen literary quote which is a rather nice touch.

The Directory of Gardening Personalities is an index of botanists, plantsmen, landscapers, gardeners and writers who have shaped the history of garden design. Where relevant, there is a link to gardens in the tour.

This work in progress is already huge and contains many quotes, garden writings, poetry, commentary and reflections on gardening. There's also a massive selection of links to sites covering every aspect of gardening, and a fascinating timeline of garden history which lists books, events and main characters and includes links to related websites.

www.gardenworld.co.uk
Gardenworld UK

Overall rating: ★ ★ ★			
Classification:	Information	**Readability:**	★ ★ ★
Updating:	Continually	**Reliability:**	★ ★ ★
Navigation:	★ ★ ★	**Speed:**	★ ★

UK

The chief use for this site is the UK Garden Centre Database, which allows you to search for garden centres or nurseries in a chosen location by name, county, postcode, facilities, services, products or other keywords. This should keep improving as more garden centres register.

The rest of the site offers limited listings of items such as **Plant and Product Suppliers** and **New Products**.

www.nccpg.org.uk
National Council for the Conservation of Plants and Gardens

Overall rating: ★ ★ ★			
Classification:	Information	**Readability:**	★ ★ ★
Updating:	Varies	**Reliability:**	★ ★ ★
Navigation:	★ ★ ★	**Speed:**	★ ★ ★ ★

UK

This site offers an introduction to the work of the NCCPG, administrators of the National Plant Collections Scheme, with information on their conservation work other associated websites and national plant collections. The site is a little haphazard in design: the page layout is not always clear and text is not always where you'd expect it to be. The navigation links can also be a misleading and you may find it more useful to use the browser's back button. Updating appears to be sporadic, with some areas up-to-date and others a season behind, at the time of writing.

SPECIAL FEATURES

Most of the information is to be found by clicking on the **News** button at the top of the home page.

Lost and Found describes the work of the council and the difficulties of tracing 'lost' plants.

National Plant Collections lists websites and contact details of collection holders.

Plant Collection of the Month was interesting and well-illustrated, although not up-to-date when we visited.

Publications produced by the Council are available to buy online, and you can join online too.

Chapter 7

Gardening for
Different Abilities

Special Needs

There's little or no UK web-presence for gardeners with disabilities, but these few sites cross the Atlantic well, are warmly enabling, and full of ideas borne of experience. They each include a number of links you may want to pursue.

www.gardenforever.com
Garden Forever

Overall rating: ★ ★ ★ ★			
Classification: Homepage		**Readability:**	★ ★ ★ ★
Updating: Unclear		**Reliability:**	★ ★ ★ ★
Navigation: ★ ★ ★ ★		**Speed:**	★ ★ ★ ★

CAN

A small but encouraging site which covers gardening for people of all ages, abilities and lifestyles including articles on gardening for those with health or mobility problems, and the therapeutic effects of gardening. Each is accompanied by information on the author and contact details. It's a good resource for those with special gardening needs, and has a good links page too. Articles are listed on the home page or the two archives on articles and tips. Text is exceptionally clear but more photos would be a helpful addition.

SPECIAL FEATURES
There are two sections, **Articles** and **Tips**, both holding a good amount of information relevant to gardeners with different abilities.

Articles has features on designing and planning gardens for special requirements, for example a sensual garden, gardens for those with impaired vision, memorial gardens. **Tips** is helpful to those gardening with limited strength, and there's advice on choosing tools, watering container gardens etc.

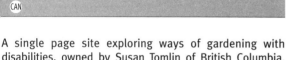

www.geocities.com/Heartland/Flats/1391/disabled.html
Susan's Disabled Gardening Page

Overall rating: ★ ★ ★			
Classification: Homepage		**Readability:**	★ ★ ★
Updating: Occasionally		**Reliability:**	★ ★ ★
Navigation: ★ ★ ★		**Speed:**	★ ★ ★ ★

CAN

www.suite101.com/welcome.cfm/enabling_garden
Suite 101 Enabling Garden

Overall rating: ★ ★ ★			
Classification: Magazine		**Readability:**	★ ★ ★ ★
Updating: Monthly		**Reliability:**	★ ★ ★ ★
Navigation: ★ ★ ★ ★		**Speed:**	★ ★ ★

US

A single page site exploring ways of gardening with disabilities, owned by Susan Tomlin of British Columbia. There is much personal testimony and details of how she continues to garden in spite of her decreasing mobility and use of a wheelchair. There's an illustrated list of easy-care plants and lots of advice on container gardening.

This is part of the Suite 101 family of gardening sites, which focuses on gardening for the physically challenged. (Also see p.19).

Kids

The UK lags way behind America when it comes to childrens' sites, and gardening is no exception. The wonderful University of Illinois and Michigan State University do masses for kids, and although these are our favourites, there are more; just follow the links on their sites.

www.urbanext.uiuc.edu/worms/
Adventures of Herman the Worm

Overall rating: ★ ★ ★ ★ ★			
Classification:	Information	**Readability:**	★ ★ ★ ★ ★
Updating:	Occasionally	**Reliability:**	★ ★ ★ ★ ★
Navigation:	★ ★ ★ ★ ★	**Speed:**	★ ★ ★ ★

US

This is a fantastic site from the University of Illinois which teaches kids all about soil science from the worm's eye view of Squirmin' Herman. It covers many aspects of worms and soil including worm anatomy in **My Anatomy** and classification in **My Family Tree**. It's fun, bright, easy-to-use site that includes animated graphics, interactive games, quizzes and extension links to other pages and sites. There is lots of information on starting a worm bin and email support if you decide to take the plunge.

This site is designed to allow children to navigate successfully by themselves, and it's made easy and fun to get around.

www.urbanext.uiuc.edu/gpe/index.html
The Great Plant Escape

Overall rating: ★ ★ ★ ★ ★	
Classification: Information	**Readability:** ★ ★ ★
Updating: Occasionally	**Reliability:** ★ ★ ★ ★
Navigation: ★ ★ ★ ★	**Speed:** ★ ★ ★ ★ ★

US

A carrot called Bud and a pea called Sprout help Detective Le Plant solve plant life mysteries. Information, quizzes, a glossary and activities are all presented in a lively, creative format for older primary school kids. An excellent site.

www.4hgarden.msu.edu/tour/index.html
The 4H Children's Garden

Overall rating: ★ ★ ★ ★	
Classification: Information	**Readability:** ★ ★ ★ ★
Updating: Seasonally	**Reliability:** ★ ★ ★ ★ ★
Navigation: ★ ★ ★ ★ ★	**Speed:** ★ ★ ★

US

This site is of definite interest to those planning or creating a garden designed for children as well as older children who enjoy gardening and you can take a tour round any of 56 themed gardens for children at Michigan State University. Instructions are clear and simple, just click on the large site map to visit one of the gardens.

There are a lot of illustrations on the site, so it takes a while to download.

Netscape Navigator is recommended although we found Internet Explorer to be adequate. QuickTime plug-in and VR component are required for the videos.

SPECIAL FEATURES

The garden is divided into eight different sections: Sunburst Area, Amphitheater, Treehouse, Rainbow Area, Butterfly Area, Maze, Pond and Chimes Area. These are then subdivided again into separate theme gardens with delightful sounding names such as: Storybook Garden, Enchanted Garden, Pizza Garden, Performing Plants Garden, Peter Rabbit Garden. Each can be explored in photos and descriptive text or by viewing a video in QuickTime. There is a list of plants used to create the gardens.

www.4hgarden.msu.edu/kids/pizza/obackground.swf

The Garden Pizza Place

Overall rating: ★ ★ ★			
Classification:	Information	**Readability:**	★ ★ ★
Updating:	Occasionally	**Reliability:**	★ ★ ★ ★
Navigation:	★ ★ ★	**Speed:**	★ ★ ★

US

A short, sweet, interactive site from the Michigan State University which shows younger kids what's needed to make a pizza and lets them have a go at working out what the different plants (wheat, tomatoes) need for healthy cultivation.

www.arnprior.com/kidsgarden/index.htm

Kids Valley Garden

Overall rating: ★ ★ ★			
Classification:	Information	**Readability:**	★ ★
Updating:	Occasionally	**Reliability:**	★ ★ ★ ★
Navigation:	★ ★ ★	**Speed:**	★ ★ ★ ★

US

A fairly basic site that provides good information for youngsters, though it may appear overwhelming at first glance due to the emphasis on text rather than pictures. British children may need help with the US terminology.

SPECIAL FEATURES

The homepage is designed as a tree: page links rest in the branches. There are features on **Planning**, **Planting**, and **Keeping Plants Healthy**, and more specific information on **Flowers**, **Veggies** and **Herbs**.

Chapter 8

Forums

Forums

Although there are a fair number of forums, chat rooms and newsgroups for gardeners, this form of online communication hasn't taken off to the same extent that it has in other subject areas. What there is tends to be US-based, although the small number of UK gardeners who use the sites is increasing all the time. It's a sociable and friendly way to communicate, and as in real life, gardeners seem to be generous with their time and happy to share their experiences.

www.gardenweb.com
GardenWeb

Overall rating: ★ ★ ★ ★ ★			
Classification:	Forum	Readability:	★ ★ ★ ★
Updating:	Continually	Reliability:	★ ★ ★
Navigation:	★ ★ ★ ★ ★	Speed:	★ ★ ★ ★

US

GardenWeb is the biggest and most comprehensive forum service for gardeners on the net. There are over 100 forums covering an enormous range of subjects, related either to location, plant type or gardening style. Both exploring and using the forums is made simple, and is clearly explained for the new user. There is a useful test forum where nonsense may be posted in order to acquaint oneself with the procedure without appearing foolish. It is a little unclear how messages are listed on the boards, although they are easy to read and latest messages appear first. (Also see p.123.)

SPECIAL FEATURES

The main page lists forums by type, topic, plant, or alphabetically by title. There are forums dedicated to gardening in the UK, a European plant and seed exchange, and others devoted to every popular garden plant and many different types of gardening. Posting or responding to a message involves the filling out of a simple on-screen form, and you can choose to be notified by email when you receive a reply. Anyone can take part, and there's no need to subscribe or register. The community is generally extremely responsive and friendly, and it shouldn't be too long before you make a helpful contact.

www.gardentown.com
Garden Town

Overall rating: ★ ★ ★ ★

Classification:	Forum	**Readability:**	★ ★ ★ ★
Updating:	Continually	**Reliability:**	★ ★ ★
Navigation:	★ ★ ★ ★	**Speed:**	★ ★ ★ ★

US

www.vg.com
Virtual Garden

Overall rating: ★ ★ ★

Classification:	Forum	**Readability:**	★ ★ ★
Updating:	Continually	**Reliability:**	★ ★ ★
Navigation:	★ ★ ★	**Speed:**	★ ★

US

An active and very friendly site hosting a general discussion board as well as one entirely devoted to gardening topics. There are a number of UK users as well as others from all over the world. From the homepage, select the required forum; within each, navigation is simple, and the posting procedure is foolproof. Messages are posted chronologically under a short title and an indication of the number of responses is given.

SPECIAL FEATURES

Both forums are well used, and have a friendly community feel. To post, either click on **Post Message** to start a new thread, or simply make a response.

Sage Hall deals with all garden-related subject matter, including problem-solving, identification, and some general chat. It is warm and relaxed, and response times are good.

Gazebo is a general and very sociable forum where any subject within reason can be aired and explored by the gardening community who use it. New users are always welcome.

There's also a plant dictionary and general compendium of useful tips by and for site users.

Virtual Garden hosts a good number of gardening forums, many of which are relevant to the UK gardener, although they're mostly used by US residents. To use the forums, click on the **Let's talk Dirt** link on the home page, which leads you to a list of discussion topics. There is a file and folder system within each topic, which allows you to further define your area of interest. A test forum is provided for practising your technique. The system needs improvement in highlighting new messages and threads, which are otherwise difficult to identify. (Also see p.17.)

SPECIAL FEATURES

Although you must be a registered member to post or reply to a message, guest access is available to browse the forums. Registering is free and affords other on-site benefits. To post, click on 'Add discussion' where you'll be prompted for a title and message.

Response times vary depending on the user traffic of the forum. The system was being updated at the time of reviewing, and some of the difficulties may well have been addressed.

www.gardenersworld.beeb.com
Gardener's World

Overall rating: ★ ★ ★		
Classification: Forum	Readability:	★
Updating: Varies	Reliability:	★ ★ ★ ★
Navigation: ★	Speed:	★

UK

At the time of writing, the BBC forum software was in the process of being updated, and a new system promised in early spring. The previous forum was reasonably active and easy to use and it's likely that the new one will be up to a good standard.

Online Chat

The best opportunity for live garden-based chat we have found is hosted by **www.garden.com** (see Essential Sites, p.16) and is easily found in the **Our Community** section. Depending on your browser's specifications, you can elect to use either a java or html format. There's nearly always someone online, and most people seem friendly and helpful. A wide range of ages take part, and new 'chatters', who are made very welcome, visit frequently. Although the bulk of the conversation is on gardening, the community is very sociable, and subjects may take surprising turns.

Chapter 9

Worth a Look...

Miscellany

Some of these sites may make you smile, others may not be your cup of tea at all, but it's good to see a few sites breaking the rules and introducing some wit and mystery to the generally very tasteful and polite world of web gardening.

www.gothic.net/~malice
Gothic Gardening

Overall rating: ★ ★ ★ ★			
Classification: Homepage		**Readability:**	★ ★ ★ ★
Updating: Unclear		**Reliability:**	★ ★ ★
Navigation: ★ ★ ★ ★		**Speed:**	★ ★ ★

US

'...From frightful blooms, rank odors seep Bats and beasties fly and creep...' A spooky site, deadly serious about the business of gothic gardening and extremely well organised, once you have got used to reading from a black background.

SPECIAL FEATURES

Theme Gardens lists plants and ideas for planning such gardens as The Garden of Deadly Delights, The Witches Garden, and Gardening for Bats.

Ye Olde Gothick Herbal gives history, folklore and sometimes recipes for plants with gothic associations.

Gothic Plant Tales includes excerpts from Myths and Legends of Flowers, Fruit, Trees and Plants, such as The Apple of Immortality and The Blood Tree.

This dark, sometimes chilling site, dedicated to gardening for goths, is compulsive reading.

www.home.golden.net/~dhobson/
Garden Humour

Overall rating: ★ ★ ★			
Classification:	Homepage	**Readability:**	★ ★ ★
Updating:	Daily	**Reliability:**	not applicable
Navigation:	★ ★ ★	**Speed:**	★ ★ ★

CAN

There's nothing remotely serious about this site from David Hobson, a Yorkshireman living in Ontario who's also a published author and public speaker. Pages and pages of wacky and amusing stuff including a diary updated daily which is impressive enough, and an hilarious guide to identifying bugs in your garden.

www.talkingplants.com
Ketzel Levine's Talking Plants

Overall rating: ★ ★ ★			
Classification:	Homepage	**Readability:**	★ ★ ★ ★
Updating:	Occasionally	**Reliability:**	★ ★ ★ ★
Navigation:	★ ★ ★ ★	**Speed:**	★ ★ ★ ★

US

Ketzel Levine is contributing editor for the well-respected Horticulture magazine. She is bold, sassy, passionate about plants and literally crazy about gardening and this completely mad and very funny online magazine is written in the style of a trashy society journal.

SPECIAL FEATURES

Interview of the week features such famous gardeners as Barbie (who grows American Beautyberry and Fuchsia magellanica 'The Bride') and Joan of Arc (who favours Fireweed and Smokebush).

Dear Diary is an occasional series of entries on love, life and gardening.

Plant Profiles reveals in intimate, blushing details why, when and how to grow the hottest garden plants.

This site breaks the mould with its quirky, brash and often hilarious look at gardening.

http://members.aol.com/compgeek35/planting.htm
Plant by the Moon

Overall rating: ★ ★ ★			
Classification:	Homepage	**Readability:**	★ ★ ★
Updating:	Unclear	**Reliability:**	★ ★
Navigation:	★ ★ ★	**Speed:**	★ ★ ★

US

www.panplanet.com/garden/plantmoon.html
Planting by the moon's phase

Overall rating: ★ ★			
Classification:	Homepage	**Readability:**	★ ★
Updating:	n/a	**Reliability:**	★ ★
Navigation:	★ ★ ★	**Speed:**	★ ★ ★

AUS

This small site is devoted to the ancient practise of 'planting by the moon' and gives indications on what to plant when the moon is in its different phases. There's also a chart listing the best jobs to undertake in the garden according to which sign of the zodiac the moon is in.

More moon information can be found on this site, which explains the importance of synchronising phases with signs and seasons.

OTHER SITES OF INTEREST

The Bonsai Site
www.bonsaisite.com
An easy to use site with stacks of information on bonsai history, techniques, maintenance and plant profiles.

The British Mycological Society
www.ulst.ac.uk/faculty/science/bms
A rather heavy, difficult to read site which is nonetheless full of useful information including links to local groups and and references for identification.

Internet Glossary

A **Accelerators** Add-on programs, which speed up browsing.

Acceptable Use Policy These are the terms and conditions of using the internet. They are usually set by organisations, who wish to regulate an individual's use of the internet. For example, an employer might issue a ruling on the type of email which can be sent from an office.

Access Provider A company which provides access to the internet, usually via a dial-up account. Many companies such as AOL and Dircon charge for this service, although there are an increasing number of free services such as Freeserve, Lineone and Tesco.net. Also known as an Internet Service Provider.

Account A user's internet connection, with an Access/Internet Service Provider, which usually has to be paid for.

Acrobat Reader Small freely-available program, or web browser plug-in, which lets you view a Portable Document Format (PDF) file.

Across Lite Plug-in which allows you to complete crossword puzzles online.

Address Location name for email or internet site, which is the online equivalent of a postal address. It is usually composed of a unique series of words and punctuation, such as *my.name@myhouse.co.uk*. See also URL.

America Online (AOL) World's most heavily subscribed online service provider.

Animated GIF Low-grade animation technique used on websites.

ASCII Stands for American Standard Code for Information Interchange, It is a coding standard which all computers can recognise, and ensures that if a character is entered on one part of the internet, the same character will be seen elsewhere.

ASCII Art Art made of letters and other symbols. Because it is made up of simple text, it can be recognised by different computers.

ASDL Stands for Asynchronous Digital Subscriber Line, which is a high speed copper wire which will allow rapid transfer of information. Not widely in use at moment, though the government is pushing for its early introduction.

Attachment A file included with an email, which may be composed of text, graphics and sound. Attachments are encoded for transfer across the internet, and can be viewed in their original form by the recipient. An attachment is the equivalent of putting a photograph with a letter in the post.

B **Bookmark** A function of the Netscape Netvigator browser which allows you to save a link to your favourite web pages, so that you can return straight there at a later date, without having to re-enter the address. Favourites in internet Explorer is the same thing.

BPS Abbreviation of Bits Per Second, which is a measure of the speed at which information is transferred or downloaded.

Browse Common term for looking around the web. See also Surfing.

Browser A generic term for the software that allows users to move and look around the Web. Netscape Navigator and

Internet Explorer are the ones that most people are familiar with, and they account for 97 percent of web hits.

Bulletin Board Service A BBS is a computer with a telephone connection, which allows you direct contact to upload and download information and converse with other users, via the computer. It was the forerunner to the online services and virtual communities of today.

Cache A temporary storage space on the hard drive of your computer, which stores downloaded websites. When you return to a website, information is retrieved from the cache and displayed much more rapidly. However, this information may not be the most recent version for sites which are frequently updated and you will need to reload the Website address for these.

Chat Talking to other users on the web in real time, but with typed, instead of spoken words. Special software such as ICQ or MIRC is required before you can chat.

Chat Room An internet channel which allows several people to type in their messages, and talk to one another over the internet.

Clickstream The trail left as you 'click' your way around the web.

Content The material on a website that actually relates to the site, and is hopefully of interest or value. Things like adverts are not considered to be part of the content. The term is also used to refer to information on the internet that can be seen by users, as opposed to programming and other background information.

Cookie A cookie is a nugget of information sometimes sent by websites to your hard drive when you visit. They contain such details as what you looked at, what you ordered, and can add more information, so that the website can be customized to suit you.

Cybercafe Cafe where you can use a computer terminal to browse the net for a small fee.

Cyberspace When first coined by the sci-fi author William Gibson, it meant a shared hallucination which occured when people logged on to computer networks. Now, it refers to the virtual space you're in when on the internet.

Dial Up A temporary telephone connection to your ISP's computer and how you make contact with your ISP, each time you log onto the Internet.

Domain The part of an Internet address which identifies an individual computer, and can often be a business or person's name. For example, in the goodwebguide.com the domain name is theGoodWebGuide.

Download Transfer of information from an Internet server to your computer.

Dynamic HTML The most recent version of the HTML standard.

Ecash Electronic cash, used to make transactions on the internet.

Ecommerce The name for business which is carried out over the internet.

Email Mail which is delivered electronically over the internet. They are usually comprised of text messages, but can contain illustrations, music and animations. Mail is sent to an email address, which is the internet equivalent of a postal address.

Encryption A process whereby information is scrambled to produce a 'coded message', so that it can't be read whilst in transit on the internet. The recipient must have decryption software in order to read the message.

Expire Term referring to newsgroup postings which are automatically deleted after a fixed period of time.

Ezine Publication on the web, which is updated regularly.

FAQ Stands for frequently asked questions and is a common section on websites where the most common enquiries and their answers are archived.

Frame A method which splits web pages into several windows.

FTP/File Transfer Protocol Standard method for transporting files across the internet.

GIF/Graphics Interchange Format A format in which graphics are compressed, and a popular method of putting images onto the internet, as they take little time to download.

Gopher The gopher was the precursor of the world wide web and consisted of archives accessed through a menu, usually organised by subject.

GUI/Graphical User Interface. This is the system which turns binary information into the words and images format you can see on your computer screen. For example, instead of seeing the computer language which denotes the presence of your toolbar, you actually see a toolbar.

Hackers A term used to refer to expert programmers who used their skills to break into computer systems, just for the fun of it. Nowadays the word is more commonly associated with computer criminals, or Crackers.

Header Basic indication of what's in an email: who it's from, when it was sent, and what it's about.

Hit When a file is downloaded from a website it is referred to as a 'hit'. Measuring the number of hits is a rough method of counting how many people visit a website. Except that it's not wholly accurate as one website can contain many files, so one visit by an individual may generate several hits.

Homepage Most usually associated with a personal site, produced by an individual, but can also refer to the first page on your browser, or the first page of a website.

Host Computer on which a website is stored. A host computer may store several websites, and usually has a fast powerful connection to the internet. Also known as a Server.

HTML/Hypertext Mark-Up Language The computer code used to construct web pages.

HTTP/Hypertext Transfer Protocol The protocol for moving HTML files across the web.

Hyperlink A word or graphic formatted so that when you click on it, you move from one area to another. See also hypertext.

Hypertext Text within a document which is formatted so it acts as a link from one page to another, or from one document to another.

Image Map A graphic which contains hyperlinks.

Interface What you actually see on the computer screen.

Internet One or more computers connected to one another is an internet (lower case i). The Internet is the biggest of all the internets. and consists of a worldwide collection of interconnected computer networks.

Internet Explorer One of the most popular pieces of browser software, produced by Microsoft.

Internet Relay Chat See Chat.

Intranet A network of computers, which works in the same way as an internet, but for internal use, such as within a corporation.

ISDN/Integrated Services Digital Network Digital telephone line which facilitates very fast connections and can transfer larges amounts of data. It can carry more than one form of data at once.

ISP/Internet Service Provider See Access Provider.

Java Programming language which can be used to create interactive multimedia effects on webpages. The language is used to create programmes known as *applets* that add features such as animations,

sound and even games to websites.

Javascript A scripting language which, like Java, can be used to add extra multimedia features. However, in contrast with Java it does not consist of separate programmes. Javascript is embedded into the HTML text and can interpreted by the browser, provided that the user has a javascript enabled browser.

JPEG Stands for 'Joint Photographic Experts Group' and is the name given to a type of format which compresses photos, so that they can be seen on the web.

Kill file A function which allows a user to block incoming information from unwanted sources. Normally used on email and newsreaders.

LAN/Local Area Network A type of internet, but limited to a single area, such as an office.

Login The account name or password needed to access a computer system.

Link Connection between web pages, or one web document and another, which are accessed via formatted text and graphic.

Mailing List A discussion group which is associated with a website. Participants send their emails to the site, and it is copied and sent by the server to other individuals on the mailing list.

Modem A device for converting digital data into analogue signals for transmission along standard phone lines. The usual way for home users to connect to the internet or log into their email accounts. May be internal (built into the computer) or external (a desk-top box connected to the computer).

MP3 A compressed music file format, which has almost no loss of quality although the compression rate may be very high.

Netscape Popular browser, now owned by AOL.

Newbie Term for someone new to the Internet. Used perjoratively of newcomers to bulletin boards or chat, who commit the sin of asking obvious questions or failing to observe the netiquette.

Newsgroup Discussion group amongst Internet users who share a mutual interest. There are thousands of newsgroups covering every possible subject.

Offline Not connected to the internet via a telephone line.

Online Connected to the internet via a telephone line.

Offline Browsing A function of the browser software, which allows the user to download pages and read them whilst offline.

Online Service Provider Similar to an access provider, but provides addtional features such as live chat.

PDF/Portable Document Format A file format created by Adobe for offline reading of brochures, reports and other documents with complex graphic design, which can be read by anyone with Acrobat Reader.

Plug-in Piece of software which adds more functions (such as playing music or video) to another, larger software program.

POP3/Post Office Protocol An email protocol that allows you to pick up your mail from any location on the web.

Portal A website which offers many services, such as search engines, email and chat rooms, and to which people are likely to return to often . ISPs such as Yahoo and Alta Vista provide portal sites which are the first thing you see when you log on, and in theory act as gateways to the rest of the web.

Post/Posting Information sent to a usenet group, bulletin board, message board or by email.

PPP/Point to Point Protocol The agreed way of sending data over dial-up connections, so that the user's computer, the modem and the Internet Server can all recognise it. It is the protocol which allows you to get online.

Protocol Convention detailing a set of actions that computers in a network must follow so that they can understand one another.

Query Request for specific information from a database.

R **RAM /Random Access Memory** Your computer's short term memory.

Realplayer G2 A plug-in program that allows you to view video in real-time and listen to sound and which is becoming increasingly important for web use.

Router A computer program which acts as an interface between two networks, and decides how to route information.

S **Searchable Database** A database on a website which allows the user to search for information, usually be keyword.

Search Engine Programs which enable web users to search for pages and sites using keywords. They are usually to be found on portal sites and browser homepages. Infoseek, Alta Vista and Lycos are some of the popular search engines.

Secure Transactions Information transfers which are encrypted so that only the sender and recipient have access to the uncoded message, so that the details within remain private. The term is most commonly used to refer to credit card transactions, although other information can be sent in a secure form.

Server A powerful computer that has a permanent fast connection to the internet. Such computers are usually owned by companies and act as host computers for websites.

Sign-on To connect to the internet and start using one of its facilities.

Shareware Software that doesn't have to be paid for or test version of software that the user can access for free, as a trial before buying it.

Standard A style which the whole of the computer industry has agreed upon. Industry standards mean that hardware and software produced by the various different computer companies will work with one another.

Surfing Slang for looking around the Internet, without any particular aim, following links from site to site.

T **TLA/Three Letter Acronyms** Netspeak for the abbreviations of net jargon, such as BPS (Bits Per Second) and ISP (Internet Service Provider).

U **Upload** To send files from your computer to another one on the internet. When you send an email you are uploading a file.

URL/Uniform Resource Locator Jargon for an address on the internet, such as www.thegoodwebguide.co.uk.

Usenet A network of newsgroups, which form a worldwide system, on which anyone can post 'news'.

V **Virtual Community** Name given to a congregation of regular mailing list/ newsgroup users.

VRML/Virtual Reality Modeling Language Method for creating 3D environments on the web. On a

Wallpaper Description of the sometimes hectic background patterns which appear behind the text on some websites.

Web Based Email/Webmail Email accounts such as Hotmail and Rocketmail, which are accessed via an Internet browser, rather than an email program such as Outlook Express. Webmail has to be typed whilst the user is online, but can accessed from anywhere on the Web.

Webmaster A person responsible for a web server. May also be known as System Administrator.

Web Page Document which forms one part of a website (though some sites are a single page), usually formatted in HTML.

Web Ring Loose association of websites which are usually dedicated to the same subject and often contain links to one another.

Website A collection of related web pages which often belong to an individual or organisation and are about the same subject.

World Wide Web The part of the Internet which is easy to get around and see. The term is often mistakely interchanged with Internet, though the two are not the same. If the Internet is a shopping mall, with shops, depots, and delivery bays, then the web is the actual shops which the customers see and use.

Index

How to use your CD

Now we've whetted your appetite for the sites reviewed in this book, we can help you to visit them quickly and easily. By registering on thegoodwebguide site, you will be able to use the hotlinks to all the sites listed, so you just click and go. You can also read the latest versions of reviews and see what we think of new sites that have been launched since the book went to press. If you wish, you can even have the updates emailed to you.

INSTALLATION INSTRUCTIONS FOR PC USERS
Insert the CD enclosed with this book into your CD drive of your PC. A welcome screen will appear with two buttons:

The goodwebguide button To register your purchase of a Good Web Guide book and to receive free updates of the reviews in the book and reviews of the latest sites, click on this button. When you've registered you can click straight through to any of the sites listed. You must have an internet connection to do this. If you are not already signed up with an internet service, you will need to install the LineOne software first.

If you click on the goodwebguide button you will be taken to a registration page where you will be asked to confirm which title in the series you have bought and to register your details. You then have free access to the updates of the website reviews in this book and to new reviews. You will also have access to the rest of the goodwebguide website.

LineOne button If you would like access to the internet you can click on this button to install LineOne's free ISP (internet service provider) software. You will need a modem to have internet access. If you already have an internet connection (ISP) you can still install LineOne as an alternative provider.

A To join LineOne just click on the LineOne button. When the first screen appears you have a choice: If you are a new user and wish to load Internet Explorer 5 as your browser, select 'Join Now'. On the next screen, select 'Go!' and you will be taken to the Microsoft installation process.

B To join immediately, without installing a browser, click 'Join Now' and then choose 'custom' to go straight to registration.

From the 'Welcome to LineOne' screen, click 'Go' and follow the on-screen instructions.

MAC USERS
This CD is not suitable for Apple Macintosh computers. For Free LineOne Mac Software call free on 0800 111 210.

RETURNING TO THE GOOD WEB GUIDE
Once you've connected to the internet, you can either type www.thegoodwebguide.co.uk into your browser to go directly to our website, or re-insert your CD and click on the goodwebguide button.

SUPPORT
If you have any problems call the LineOne support number.
CALL 0906 30 20 100
(calls may be monitored or recorded for training purposes) 24 hours, 365 days a year. Calls charged at 50p/minute or email support@lineone.net for free support.

Other titles in thegoodwebguide series include

Parenting ISBN 1-903282-03-9

Gardening ISBN 1-903282-00-4

Money ISBN 1-903282-02-0

Food ISBN 1-903282-01-2

Forthcoming Good Web Guide titles

The Good Web Guide to Wine
ISBN 1-903282-04-7

The Good Web Guide to Travel
ISBN 1-903282-05-5

The Good Web Guide to Genealogy
ISBN 1-903282-06-3

The Good Web Guide to Health
ISBN 1-903282-08-X